AMERICAN PAINTINGS
IN
THE FERDINAND HOWALD COLLECTION

AMERICAN PAINTINGS
IN
THE FERDINAND HOWALD COLLECTION

CATALOGUE PREPARED BY MARCIA TUCKER

WITH RESEARCH ASSISTANCE AND BIOGRAPHIES BY KASHA LINVILLE

INTRODUCTION BY

EDGAR P. RICHARDSON

THE COLUMBUS GALLERY OF FINE ARTS

Library of Congress Catalogue Card Number 72–95250

Printed in the United States of America

FOREWORD

This catalogue was made possible by a grant from the Ford Foundation under its Museum Catalogue Program. I would like to thank Mrs. Marcia Thompson of the Ford Foundation for her cooperation and advice. Additional grants were made by the Nesbitt-Westwater Fund of the Columbus Foundation and the Charles Y. and Frances N. Lazarus Foundation. The balance of the expense was paid by The Columbus Gallery of Fine Arts. I would like to thank Edgar P. Richardson for his introduction, Marcia Tucker for her excellent work in preparing the catalogue, and Bert Clarke for his design. This catalogue should bring to the American paintings in the Howald Collection the renown they so richly deserve.

MAHONRI SHARP YOUNG
Director

ACKNOWLEDGEMENTS

I would like to express my thanks to those who helped with the preparation and realization of this catalogue.

Mr. Mahonri S. Young, Director of the Gallery, offered invaluable encouragement and advice. The staff of the museum was most hospitable to us, and made obscure records and documents available.

I am grateful to Miss Laura Dean, Mrs. Deborah Freedman and Mrs. Carol Shachtman, who assisted with the research and typing of the manuscript, and to Miss Ann Ohlmacher who contributed the notes on John Marin. Mrs. Evelyn Semler of the Museum of Modern Art Library in New York was most helpful in locating reference material. I am especially indebted to Bert Clarke for his continued interest and advice.

Above all, I would like to express my deep gratitude to Mrs. Kasha Linville, who helped to research, edit and revise the catalogue, and whose dedication and skill saw the work to completion.

MARCIA TUCKER

Contents

The Ferdinand Howald Collection

No one knows what makes a great collector. Outstanding ability is rare in any field and in none, perhaps, more so than in the peculiar blend of sensibility, visual perception and acquisitiveness that we call collecting art.

Ferdinand Howald was, in my judgment, a great collector. He was an unlikely candidate for that distinction. He was born in Wangen-am-Aar, Switzerland, September 2, 1856, the son of a blacksmith. His father emigrated by sailing ship to America in 1856, settling first on a farm at Etna, near Columbus, Ohio. Later he moved to Columbus, which had a considerable colony of German-speaking immigrants, and worked for the Hertenstein Stove Company. He died while Ferdinand was in college.

The Howalds were a close-knit, clannish family. There were seven children, Maria, Rosa, Elise, Emma, Ferdinand, Frederick and Arnold. Two of the sisters became teachers in the Columbus schools and never married; Rosa stayed at home to keep house for the family; all helped send Ferdinand to college. He graduated as a bachelor of science in the first class from the new Ohio State University (1878) and received his degree as mining engineer in 1881. He went into the coal mining industry in the New River district of West Virginia. A thrifty Swiss, he saved money and was able to buy Chesapeake and Ohio Railroad stock at a very low figure during the panic of 1893. This laid the foundation for his later independence. He was able to establish himself as an owner-operator of the Rush Run Coal & Coke Co. Other companies were organized until there were nine mines under his management, which in 1903 he consolidated in The New River Smokeless Coal Co.

In the early nineteen hundreds there was an explosion in the Red Ash mine, trapping a number of miners underground. Howald and another supervisor started into the mine in an attempt at rescue but were prevented by the miners, who told the two white-collar men: we take care of our own. While the rescue crew was in the mine, a second explosion took place and many more lives were lost. Whether this was the cause or the occasion is not known, but shortly thereafter, in 1906, Howald sold out his mining interests and retired with a comfortable fortune, still a comparatively young man. He moved to New York City, traveled, yet kept close to his family in Ohio. He built a large house on Park Drive in Columbus where the entire family lived, his sister Rosa running the house but Ferdinand definitely the head of the clan on his regular visits home.

He never married. In the mining towns of West Virginia there was little to do in the evening. He read a great deal and developed the habit of studious self-sufficiency in solitude that remained with him all his life. He left behind the memory of a dignified and reserved man having strong family loyalties, but one whom few if any people outside his family called by his first name. Charles Daniel, the art dealer in New York from whom Howald made most of his purchases, recalled that he never came into the gallery in the company of another person; he was always by himself. In his profession of mining engineer he belonged to the Society of Engineers (London) and to the Legion of Honor of the American

Institute of Mining and Metallurgical Engineers, composed of those with fifty years of continuous membership; but as a collector of art he acted alone and was almost unknown.*

This was the life of one of the great collectors of American painting in the early twentieth century. Son of a Swiss blacksmith; educated in a newly founded land-grant college; living a solitary life until he was fifty in the West Virginia coal fields; trained in a precise and factual branch of technology, he was not a man whom one would expect to show a remarkable flair for collecting art. Indeed, if he were to collect at all, one would expect him to show something of his training and life-long activity as an engineer. He became instead a collector of what was then the new wave of painting whose aim was to break away from every existing habit of literal and exact representation in the arts.

To explain this by the easy solution that he began collecting after the Armory Show in 1913 introduced French Post-Impressionism and "Modernism" to the American public is no explanation at all. Nothing is more deceptive than the view from the present as one looks back upon changes of taste. Passing time simplifies the confusion and contradictions of the contemporary scene into what appears to be order, makes the haphazard seem logical and the intuitive action appear coolly rational choice. The Armory Show has been magnified by the human need for a myth. It is thus supposed that a single exhibition of two months created, and explains, the entire subsequent course of American art. It was instead a vast, confusing mélange of some 1300 exhibits by 300 artists, including the living and the dead, European and American, a few artists now considered great and a great many more now forgotten. Maurice Prendergast and Ernest Lawson, whose work Howald loved, were there; Charles Demuth and Preston Dickinson whose work he also loved, were not. Men of every trend and style from the eighteen-eighties to 1913—impressionists, post-impressionists, solitaries, the advanced and the *retardataire*, *The Eight*, the newest recruit just back with the latest word from Paris, the old guard, all were there; and, of course, a big dose of what Paris admired at that moment. Far from arousing more interest in American art, as its organizers hoped, the Armory Show turned American collectors toward French Post-Impressionism and the contemporary school of Paris. Among the new collectors appearing in the United States in the years following, Howald was almost alone in his devotion to American artists. The others, as Milton Brown points out in his study of American painting from the Armory Show to the Depression, were collectors of French art. If they bought the work of certain Americans (as did Miss Lillie Bliss, Albert C. Barnes and John Quinn), they did so because of friendship or because the Americans were echoes of a tendency in Paris in which the collector was especially interested. Howald went his way quietly, independently, ignoring the rush to Paris. The key to his taste lies elsewhere than in the Armory Show and its influence.

A small notebook among the Howald papers in the possession of his heirs is headed, in a neat, precise handwriting:

Ferdinand Howald
Catalog

It contains the record of his purchases, kept with the systematic exactness one would expect of him.

* Only one article was published about the Howald collection in his lifetime, written by Forbes Watson in *The Arts* in 1925. It reproduced a large number of pictures but is otherwise quite uninformative.

Howald's first venture into the ownership of art was the purchase, in Chicago in 1894, of three etchings by Anders Zorn, *In a Paris Omnibus*, *Zorn and his wife* and *Count G. von Rosen*. Zorn was a sensation of the Chicago World's Fair. His work, however spectacular in technique, was not difficult for his contemporaries to comprehend and the purchase tells us little about what Howald then was.

A long pause in the record follows. In January of 1913 he bought for very small sums, at an auction at the American Art Association in New York City, a portrait by John Opie, the English portraitist; a small picture ascribed to the Sienese Gothic painter Francesco Vanni; and a *Flight into Egypt* by the Venetian Cariani. In the following months he commissioned portraits of his sisters Elise and Rosa, his brother Fred and his niece Flora Shawan from Leon Kroll (who had exhibited in the Armory Show) and from Eugene Speicher and Douglas Volk (who had not). The Armory Show came in February and March of that year, attracted great attention and notoriety, and killed the Association of American Painters and Sculptors that staged it. In the autumn of 1913 Charles Daniel, who kept a cafe with his brother, and collected art in a small way, opened a gallery to show the work of some of the American painters of the new wave.

In February of 1914 Howald dropped in at Daniel's gallery—he must already have acquired the habit of visiting galleries—and saw there a painting by Edward Middleton Manigault, a brilliant, high-strung, short-lived artist, now largely forgotten. Howald inquired the price, without giving his name. A month later he wrote from Columbus that if the picture were still available, he would buy it. This was his entry into the field of art in which his collection was to be outstanding. It was a characteristic one. He was not a compulsive buyer, not a buyer on impulse. A quiet, cautious man, he bought after careful study and deliberation; but once his interest was aroused and his mind satisfied, he was firm in his affections and loyalties. He was not content to own one picture by the artists whose work he admired; he followed their work steadily, buying many, selecting with remarkably sure taste, over a period of years. Each year from 1916 to 1924 he acquired several by John Marin until he owned twenty-eight, which, as we can see in retrospect, represent Marin at his best in those years. In the same way he followed the work of Charles Demuth, Preston Dickinson, Marsden Hartley, Ernest Lawson and Maurice Prendergast, forming an admirably representative group of each.

Although Howald was to become the most important client of Charles Daniel's gallery, he was not involved with Daniel's painters from the first. From 1913 to 1916 he made purchases at exhibitions of the National Arts Club, the National Academy of Design, the New York Watercolor Club. He was abroad in 1914 but purchased nothing in Europe; instead he was one of a group of Americans who chartered a boat down the Seine to escape from the war. In 1915 he visited the Panama-Pacific Exposition, buying a few pictures by now forgotten European painters. In March, 1916, he again bought a fifteenth century Italian picture, ascribed to the school of Fra Filippo Lippi, at an auction at the American Art Association. But in December, 1915, he visited the Daniel Gallery and purchased an oil, *Winter*, by Ernest Lawson and two watercolors, *St. Malo* and *Venice* by Maurice Prendergast. After this he began to collect with enthusiasm, buying 28 paintings from Daniel in 1916 (returning one later) and 25 in 1917 (returning one later)*. This burst of collecting may perhaps have had some of its source in the darkness of the years of the battles of the Somme and Verdun, when a humane and thoughtful

* These numbers are taken from Howald's handwritten catalogue. Not all his purchases came finally to The Columbus Gallery of Fine Arts; about 100 went to his family.

mind craved to think of something fresh and unshadowed by the great catastrophe of the war. But it also represents a personal discovery, a discovery of his own direction. In these years he acquired for the first time the work of Demuth, Marin, Hartley and Preston Dickinson—also of Glackens, Luks and Rockwell Kent.

To us, looking backward, this choice may seem neither remarkable nor especially individual; but in 1916 and 1917 it was both. If a collector's taste at that time had been swayed by the Armory Show, he would have purchased A. B. Davies or Walt Kuhn, its organizers; or Max Weber who, considering himself the most important American Post-Impressionist, withdrew his pictures from the Armory in a huff because certain other painters were allowed to show a greater number than he; or painters like Alfred Maurer, Bernard Karfiol and Abraham Walkowitz, who then seemed to be the avant-garde because they looked most like the French. Howald was not unaware of this group, for he bought at this time two pictures by Sam Halpert, then just back from Paris and enjoying a reputation as a Post-Impressionist which his later career did not sustain.

Had he, on the other hand, followed the judgment of the artist juries of the big annuals, he would have purchased the work of the figure painters—Chase, Bellows, Henri or perhaps Hawthorne. The prevailing climate of American art can be judged by the big annuals, which then still dominated the scene. The Temple Gold Medal of the Pennsylvania Academy of the Fine Arts went in 1915 to Charles W. Hawthorne; in 1916 to a Philadelphian, Joseph T. Pearson; in 1917 to George Bellows; in 1918 to George Luks. This was a progressive choice compared to the awarding of the Thomas B. Clarke medal of the National Academy of Design in 1915 to Richard E. Miller, in 1916 to F. Edwin Church, in 1917 to Max Bohm. Howald was not unaware of this side of American painting. He used to visit the annual in Philadelphia, and in 1916 bought two oils by Glackens and three pastels by Luks. But he never acquired a picture by George Bellows, product of Columbus, of whom his city was so proud; he purchased instead, in 1917, three water colors by Alice Schille, a Columbus painter whose work somewhat resembled that of Prendergast. Howald's first major purchases in 1916 and 1917 thus speak for a highly idiosyncratic response to the contemporary scene. His choice seems obvious only because time has in so many instances verified his perception of quality.

Charles Daniel spoke of Howald as a man who really enjoyed pictures; who, as soon as he heard of a new painter, would come in to see his work. The list of his purchases makes it evident that he would buy a painting or two by a new talent to see if he enjoyed living with it; only painters who passed this test were represented in large number. He was certainly not influenced nor deterred by price. He purchased his first water colors by Marin in 1916 for $130 and $140 but continued until, with the rise of Marin's reputation, he was paying $1,200 in 1924. He paid $20 for a Demuth water color in 1916 and $750 for one in 1925.

But loyal as he was to talent in which he believed, his incurable reserve kept him at a distance. He knew some of the artists personally, others not. He knew Rockwell Kent and financed his trip to Alaska in 1918–19. But Kent wrote him from Arlington, Vermont, after his return: "This fall, when you return to New York, I shall hope to have a nice long talk with you. I'd like to know you well. But you are through your great reserve a difficult man to enter into familiar friendship with." He also knew Man Ray and bought his work in New York in the years 1918–20. In 1921 the artist arranged to sell Howald pictures to the amount of $500 and went to Paris on the money. There, however, he became interested in photography and stopped painting. The correspondence shows that Man Ray expected Howald to continue nonetheless as the generous supporter. When Howald realized that no new paintings would be forthcoming, that he was expected to be content to take early works left in New York which he had already seen and did not wish to own, he ceased his support. It is clear that his support was for the work, not the man.

What was Howald's point of view, his range of sensibility? His engineering training does not seem to have entered into it; he showed no preference for the literal or the precise. Radiance of hue and boldness of color pattern were central. A handsome group of Rhodian pottery, which came with his pictures to The Columbus Gallery of Fine Arts, is supporting evidence. He understood and responded to the aim of the artists of that generation to stylize nature, to create new rhythmic organizations of shape and color, to compose tightly and with strong, lively pattern.

Howald was an acute and sympathetic observer of what proved to be two of the most productive impulses in American art of the early twentieth century. One was the impulse to liberate drawing from the literal representation of nature and to find a new kind of constructive and expressive artist like John Marin; his group of that artist's work is one of the focal points of his taste. The other was the American use of the new forms and the compressed space invented by the Cubists, applying these in America to a fresh and vigorous subject matter. The large, admirably chosen group of paintings by Charles Demuth marks, in my opinion, the other pole of Howald's sympathies.

Above all, he liked his talent pure and firm. He experimented with some of the eclectic talents, numerous in the wake of the school of Paris, but these play a small role. He seems to have recognized instinctively the growth of an independent talent responding to an urge from within, rather than changing in response to the shifting tides of the art world outside.

After the war he resumed his travels and bought in Paris and in New York a few small, but excellent, examples of the contemporary painters of Paris. Daniel bought a Degas pastel for him at an auction in New York in 1921. Was the motive his fondness for Paris, a desire to round out his collection, or perhaps that he grew tired of people looking at his Marins and saying, Have you no Matisse, no Picasso, no Vlaminck? We shall never know. The French group, though excellent, remained a marginal part of his achievement.

In the nineteen twenties Alfred Stieglitz approached him. Howald appears never to have bought anything from him. They corresponded and maintained contacts for a time. When in 1926 Howald returned a picture by Georgia O'Keeffe that had been taken home on trial, communication between him and 291 Fifth Avenue came to an end. He never acquired a work by O'Keeffe. Stieglitz could not refrain from directing and exhorting; and I suspect that Howald disliked intensely to be told what he ought to admire.

In 1923 William Hekking became director of The Columbus Gallery of Fine Arts. An enthusiast for the new wave of painting, he was surprised to find a house full of it in Columbus. Hekking won Howald's interest for the gallery, which was then struggling to find money to erect its present building. "We enjoyed each other's cigars while we spoke German and became warm friends" was Hekking's comment. "I guess the fact that I could speak his mother tongue fluently was the opening for this friendship." This is too modest. Hekking was the first man in Columbus to comprehend what Howald had brought together. Before Hekking left Columbus in 1925, the reserved old collector had contributed a fifth of the money required for the new museum building and had bequeathed to it the bulk of his collection. He wanted, he said to Hekking, "to see a real art museum in Columbus." He did see one. His collection was shown for the first time publicly at the opening of the new gallery in 1931. Howald died in Columbus on March 29, 1934, at the age of seventy-eight.

Philadelphia, November, 1968 E. P. RICHARDSON

NOTE ON SOURCES

The Shawan family of Columbus owns Ferdinand Howald's own handwritten catalogue of his purchases and letters. They have some correspondence, chiefly letters written to him, of which the most important groups are from: Charles Daniel; Alarcon Hartpence, assistant in the Daniel Gallery; Alfred Stieglitz; Georgia O'Keeffe; Man Ray; Rockwell Kent; Jacques Mauny; The Columbus Gallery of Fine Arts. The only article written on the Howald Collection was by Forbes Watson in *The Arts* VIII (August, 1925), 64–81.

On Charles Daniel, the Gallery has a valuable set of notes from an interview with Mr. Daniel by Tracy Atkinson, Elizabeth J. Morris and James Slagle. Elizabeth McCausland published a useful article, "The Daniel Gallery and Modern American Art" in the *Magazine of Art*, November, 1951, pp. 280–285.

On William Hekking's role, the Gallery has a long letter of reminiscence, dated March 5, 1963. This was supplemented by a short letter to the writer, dated October, 1968.

Valuable information on the Howald family was given by Mr. David Shawan of Columbus, a grand-nephew of Mr. Howald. Other most helpful information was supplied by Mahonri Sharp Young and Edmund Kuehn of The Columbus Gallery of Fine Arts; by Mrs. K. M. Royalty, the Registrar; by the Alumni Office of the Ohio State University; by Mr. Edward Walsh of the American Institute of Mining, Metallurgical and Petroleum Engineers.

AMERICAN PAINTINGS

IN

THE FERDINAND HOWALD COLLECTION

The following abbreviated forms are used in this catalogue for frequently recurring exhibitions:

Cincinnati Art Museum, 1935
Cincinnati Art Museum, Cincinnati, Ohio, "Paintings from the Howald Collection," 6 January–3 February 1935.

Arts Club of Chicago, 1939
Arts Club of Chicago, Chicago, Illinois, "Water Colors and Pastels of Four Modern American Painters," 6–21 December 1939.

Dayton Art Institute, 1941
Dayton Art Institute, Dayton, Ohio, "Early Works from Ten Well-Known Contemporary American Painters," 2–31 December 1941.

Carnegie Institute, 1952
Carnegie Institute, Pittsburgh, Pennsylvania, "The Howald Collection from the Columbus Gallery of Fine Arts," 28 February–13 April 1952.

Philbrook Art Center, 1956
Philbrook Art Center, Tulsa, Oklahoma, "Howald Water Colors," 7–26 February 1956, and tour to Pasadena Art Institute, 11 March–11 April 1956, Fine Arts Gallery of San Diego, 20 April–27 May 1956.

Albany Institute, 1958
Albany Institute of History and Art, Albany, New York, "Howald Collection of Water Colors," 6–29 January 1958.

Walker Art Center, 1960
Walker Art Center, Minneapolis, Minnesota, "Precisionist View in American Art," 13–25 November 1960, and tour to Whitney Museum, New York, Detroit Institute of Arts, Los Angeles County Museum, San Francisco Museum of Art, 1960–1961.

University of New Mexico Art Museum, 1967
University of New Mexico Art Museum, Albuquerque, New Mexico, "Cubism, Its Impact in the United States," and tour to Marion Koogler McNay Art Institute, San Antonio, San Francisco Museum of Art, Los Angeles Municipal Art Gallery, 10 February–31 August 1967.

Museum of Fine Arts, St. Petersburg, 1968
Museum of Fine Arts, St. Petersburg, Florida, "Works from the Howald Collection," 19 April–18 May 1968.

Catalogue

*In the listing of dimensions, height precedes width. The bibliographies are selected. * indicates illustrated.*

Albert Bloch (1882–)

Born St. Louis, Missouri, 1882. Studied art at Washington University; studied in New York, 1909; in Munich and in Paris 1912. Became associated with Der Blaue Reiter in Munich. Remained in Europe 13 years. Returned to U.S. in 1922; became head of art department at University of Kansas. Exhibited with Société Anonyme.

BIBLIOGRAPHY: "Albert Bloch, Retrospective Exhibition of His Work From 1911–1955," catalogue, University of Kansas Museum of Art, September–October 1955, introductory letter by Bloch; "Albert Bloch, Exhibition of Water Colors, Drawings and Drypoints," catalogue, University of Kansas, April–June 1963, introduction by Ernst Scheyer.

1 *Veranda*. 1920. *
Oil on pasteboard, 18 × 21⅛ in. (46 × 53.5 cm.).
Monogram lower left "AB."

From the time of Block's first visit to Munich in 1909 until he returned home 12 years later, his association with Der Blaue Reiter was to have a decisive effect on his art. *Veranda*, with its shifting, tilted planes and ghostly figures, partakes of the mysterious and somewhat bitter flavor of German Expressionism. Combined here with a romantic cubist style peculiar to American avant-garde painting of the '20's, it is typical of Bloch's best work.

EXHIBITIONS: Cincinnati Art Museum, 1935; University of Kansas, Lawrence, Kansas, "Bloch Retrospective of his Work from 1911 to 1955," September–October 1955, no. 7, illus.; Whitney Museum of American Art, New York, "The Decade of the Armory Show, New Directions in American Art 1910–1920," 27 February–14 April 1963, no. 3.

REPRODUCED: *Arts*, vol. 8, August 1925, p. 88 (as *Figures and Landscape*).

Peter Blume (1906–)

Born in Russia, 1906. Family immigrated to U.S. and New York City, 1911. Began art classes at Educational Alliance in 1921 at age 15 and continued there until 1924; also at Beaux Arts Academy and Art Students League under Boardman Robinson. Rented studio on 13th Street in 1925. Spent next two years painting in New England and New York. First one-man exhibition at Daniel Gallery, New York, 1930. Opened studio in Sherman, Connecticut, in 1930. Travelled in Italy, France and England on Guggenheim Fellowship in 1932; Fellowship renewed in 1936. Painted murals for post office in Geneva, New York, and court house in Rome, Georgia. One-man show at Downtown Gallery, 1941. Travelled in Mexico, 1949; visited Italy and Sicily, 1952; took a South Pacific cruise in 1954; returned to Italy, 1956. Artist-in-residence at American Academy, Rome, 1957 and 1962.

BIBLIOGRAPHY: Soupault, P. "Un Peintre d'Amerique, Peter Blume," *La Renaissance*, XV, October 1932, pp. 157–160; Protter, Eric (ed.). *Painters on Painting*. New York, 1963.

2 *Still Life—Cyclamen No. 1*. c. 1925. *
Oil on canvas, 16⅞ × 10 in. (43 × 25.3 cm.).
Signed lower right "Peter Blume."

EXHIBITIONS: Dayton Art Institute, 1941; Carnegie Institute, 1952; American Federation of Arts, New York, "Collectors Club Meeting," May 1958; Currier Gallery of Art, Manchester, New Hampshire, "Paintings and Drawings: Peter Blume in Retrospect 1925–1964," 18 April–31 May 1964, no. 1, illus. p. 27.

3 *Home for Christmas*. c. 1926. *
Oil on canvas, 24 × 35⅞ in. (61.1 × 91.1 cm.).
Signed lower right "Peter Blume."

Home for Christmas was painted in Northampton, Massachusetts, where Blume spent some time in 1926 between trips to Maine. It is a highly unusual work for him, with none of the surrealist devices found in later paintings like *Eternal City*. The simple and rustic style which Blume used to depict this New England scene is reminiscent of American primitive painting of the late 17th century. Profile and full-face figures are silhouetted against the snow, shadows eliminated and details (as in the face) delineated with deliberate naivete. This kind of primitivism complements the severe geometry of buildings in the background, prefiguring the Precisionist crispness of his later work. The Immaculates, including Sheeler and Niles Spencer, as well as the sculptor Elie Nadelman, were exhibiting in New York during this time, and their work was likely to have influenced Blume's early style.

EXHIBITIONS: Cincinnati Art Museum, 1935; Dayton Art Institute, 1941; Art Gallery of Toronto, Grange Park, Toronto, Canadian Society of Painters in Water Color, "Museums' Choice: Paintings by Contemporary Americans," February 1945, no. 37; Carnegie Institute, 1952; Currier Gallery of Art, Manchester, New Hampshire, "Paintings and Drawings: Peter Blume in Retrospect 1925–1964," 18 April–31 May 1964, no. 3.

REPRODUCED: Goodrich, Lloyd. "New York Exhibitions," *Arts*, vol. 9, no. 5, May 1926, p. 283; Brown, Milton. *American Painting from the Armory Show to the Depression.* Princeton, 1955, p. 125.

Louis Bouché (1896–1969)

Born New York City, 1896. Studied in Paris, 1910–1915, at Académie Colarossi, Académie de la Grand Chaumière, Académie des Beaux Arts with Jules Bernard, Bernard Naudin; studied at Art Students League, New York, 1915–1916. Exhibited in first Independents show in New York in 1917; later at Daniel Gallery, 1918–1931. Painted murals in New Interior Building and Justice Building, Washington, D.C., and Radio City Music Hall, New York. Taught at Art Students League from 1943, National Academy of Design from 1951.

BIBLIOGRAPHY: "Bouché," *American Artist*, vol. 8, April 1944, pp. 14–17.

4 *Still Life with Flowers.* 1919.
Oil on canvas, 24 × 20 in. (60.9 × 50.7 cm.).
Signed and dated lower right "L. Bouché 1919."

5 *Still Life with Brown Pitcher.* 1924. *
Oil on canvas, 20 × 24 in. (50.7 × 60.9 cm.).
Signed and dated top center "Louis Bouché 1924."

EXHIBITIONS: Dayton Art Institute, 1941; Dayton Art Institute, Dayton, Ohio (one-man show), 1–31 January 1944; Cincinnati Art Museum, Cincinnati, Ohio, "An American Show," 1 October–5 November 1948, no. 14, illus.

REPRODUCED: *Arts*, vol. 8, August 1925, p. 82.

Fiske Boyd (1895–)

BIBLIOGRAPHY: "The Water Color Series; Introducing Fiske Boyd," *American Artist*, XIV, October 1950, pp. 56–57.

6 *Composition.* 1923.
Oil on canvas, 32⅛ × 24⅛ in. (81.6 × 61.2 cm.).
Signed and dated lower right "Fiske Boyd 1923."

Emile Pierre Branchard (1881–1938)

7 *Moonlight.* n.d.
Oil on pasteboard, 9⅝ × 12⅝ in. (25 × 32.1 cm.).
Signed lower right "Emile Branchard."

Charles Burchfield (1893–1967)

Born Ashtabula Harbor, Ohio, 1893. Spent childhood in Salem, Ohio. Worked as an accountant, 1911–1912. Studied at Cleveland School of Art (now Cleveland Institute) 1912–1916 under Henry G. Keller, F. N. Wilcox and William J. Eastman; one-man show there in 1916; continued to work summers as an accountant. Awarded scholarship to National Academy of Design, New York, 1916; left after attending one class. Water colors shown at Sunwise Turn Bookshop, New York. Returned to Salem, 1916, to accounting job; painted in spare time. Served in Army 1918–1919. Painted full time in the summer of 1920, with brief trips to Tennessee and New York. Moved to Buffalo, New York, 1921; worked as designer in wallpaper company. Attracted by Buffalo's post civil war architecture, he began a series of studies of buildings, which he continued until 1928. One-man show, Art Institute of Chicago, 1923. Works sold by Montross Gallery, New York, 1924–1928; Frank K. M. Rehn Gallery from 1929. Resigned from design job in 1929 to paint full time. Received *Fortune Magazine* commission to paint railroad yards at Altoona and Harrisburgh, Pennsylvania, in 1936, then sulphur and coal mines in Texas and West Virginia in 1937. Taught at Art Institute of Buffalo 1949–1952; taught advanced seminar at Buffalo Fine Arts Academy 1951–1952; summer classes at University of Minnesota 1949, Ohio University 1950, University of Buffalo 1950–1951, Ohio University 1953. Died 1967.

BIBLIOGRAPHY: McCormick, W. B. "A Small Town in Paint," *International Studio*, vol. LXXX, March 1925, pp. 466–70; Burchfield, Charles. "On the Middle Border," *Creative Art*, vol. 3, September 1928, pp. XXV–XXXII; Read, Helen A. "Charles Burchfield, a Pioneer of the New American School," *London Studio*, vol. 16, no. 91, October 1938, pp. 208–211; "Charles Burchfield; a Retrospective Exhibition of Water Colors and Oils 1916–1943," catalogue, Buffalo Fine Arts Academy, April–May 1944; Richardson, E. P. "Charles Burchfield," *Magazine of Art*, vol. 37, October 1944, pp. 208–212; George, Laverne. "Charles Burchfield," *Arts*, vol. XXX, January 1956, pp. 26–31; Baur, John I. H. *1909—Charles Burchfield.* Whitney Museum, New York, 1956; Baur, John I. H. "Fantasy and Symbolism in Charles Burchfield's Early Water Colors," *Art Quarterly*, vol. XIX, no. 1, 1956, pp. 30–40; Richardson, E. P. "Three American Painters: Sheeler, Hopper, Burchfield," *Perspectives U.S.A.*, no. 16, Summer 1956, pp. 111–119; Park, Julian and W. H. Glover (eds.). "Charles Burchfield on Art; An Interview," *Niagara Frontier*, vol. 7, no. 4, Winter 1961 (publ. by Buffalo and Erie County Historical Society), pp. 115–130; "Charles Burchfield: His Golden Year," catalogue, University of Arizona, November 1965–January 1966.

1 Albert Bloch *Veranda* 1920

5 Louis Bouché *Still Life with Brown Pitcher* 1924

2 Peter Blume *Still Life—Cyclamen No.* 1 c. 1925

3 Peter Blume *Home for Christmas* c. 1926

8 Charles Burchfield *The Visit* c. 1920–1924

9 Charles Burchfield *Winter Solstice* c. 1920–1921

10 Charles Burchfield *October* c. 1922–1924

8 *The Visit*. c. 1920–1924. *
Water color, 25⅞ × 34 in. (65.8 × 86 cm.).
Signed lower right "C. Burchfield."

In 1920, Burchfield became interested in painting the evocative qualities of American vernacular architecture. Hawthorne's theme of the deserted house and the attributes of provincial America expressed in Sherwood Anderson's books are the literary counterpart of these somber, heavily-brushed pictures of Salem, Ohio.

"A house," Burchfield wrote, "is often more moody than nature . . . In the daytime they have an astonished look; at dusk they are evil; each seems to brood over some crime . . . Each one is individual."

Once described by the critic Henry McBride as "songs of hate," such pictures owe their mood of desolation as much to the subject as to Burchfield's attitude toward it.

EXHIBITIONS: Cincinnati Art Museum, 1935; Dayton Art Institute, 1941; Carnegie Institute, 1952; Albany Institute, 1958; American Federation of Arts, New York, "Adventures in Collecting," October 1958–October 1960, no. 1; University of Arizona Art Gallery, Tucson, "Charles Burchfield: His Golden Year," 14 November 1965–9 January 1966, no. 36, illus. p. 115.

9 *Winter Solstice*. c. 1920–1921. *
Water color, 21½ × 35½ in. (54.5 × 89.8 cm.).
Signed lower right "C. Burchfield."

EXHIBITIONS: Museum of Living Art, New York University, New York, "Opening Exhibition," 13 December 1927–25 January 1928; Carnegie Institute, 1952; Albany Institute, 1958; American Federation of Arts, New York, "Adventures in Collecting," October 1958–October 1960, no. 2; University of Arizona Art Gallery, Tucson, "Charles Burchfield: His Golden Year," 14 November 1965–9 January 1966, no. 35, illus. p. 61.

REPRODUCED: *International Studio*, vol. 80, March 1925, p. 468; *Charles Burchfield*. American Artists Group monograph 13, New York, 1945; *College Art Journal*, vol. VII, no. 1, Autumn 1947, p. 9.

10 *October*. c. 1922–1924. *
Oil and gouache on pasteboard, 31¼ × 43⅝ in. (79.3 × 110.5 cm.).
Signed lower right "C. Burchfield"; on back "2 October Chas. Burchfield."

This painting may have been conceived as part of a series, never completed, for the months of the year. An intensely romantic work, it is a product of Burchfield's deep involvement with nature. *October* is unusual for this period in his career, when the artist was primarily interested in depicting the bleak, man-made environment of Buffalo, New York. where he worked as a designer for a wallpaper firm The dramatic theme of horses fleeing from a burnt and desolate forest, executed with the expressive strokes characteristic of Burchfield's style, are anomalies in an era when landscape painting remained, for the most part, academic in style and subject matter.

EXHIBITIONS: Carnegie Institute, Pittsburgh, "29th International Exhibition of Paintings," 16 October–7 December 1930, no. 107, plate 19; Dayton Art Institute, 1941; Carnegie Institute, 1952; Albany Institute, 1958; University of Arizona Art Gallery, Tucson, "Charles Burchfield: His Golden Year," 14 November 1965–9 January 1966, no. 37, illus. p. 116.

REPRODUCED: *International Studio*, vol. 80, March 1925, p. 470; *New York Herald Tribune*, 2 November 1930; *The American Magazine of Art*, vol. 21, December 1930, p. 674; Brown, Milton. *American Painting from the Armory Show to the Depression*. Princeton, 1955, p. 181; *see:* Richardson, E. P. "Charles Burchfield," *Magazine of Art*, vol. 37, October 1944, p. 210.

Arthur B. Davies (1862–1928)

Born Utica, New York, 1862. Student of Dwight Williams, 1877; studied at Chicago Academy of Design, 1878, under Roy Robertson. Travelled in Mexico as civil engineer, 1880–1882; interested in gaucho life and Spanish-Mexican church art. Studied at Art Institute of Chicago, 1882, with Charles Corwin; attended Art Students League, New York, 1886–1888. Show of works, New York, 1888, attracted attention of William Macbeth who arranged for Davies to study in Europe in 1893. Trip to California, 1905. Adviser to Lillie P. Bliss. Exhibited with *The Eight* in 1908; was instrumental in persuading Macbeth to show them. Acquired reputation by 1911 as important collector. As president of Association of American Painters and Sculptors, was primary organizer for Armory Show, 1913, and travelled to Europe to arrange the exhibition. As a result of his research in ancient Greek art in 1922, he developed theory of "inhalation" that influenced his subsequent work. Went to Europe, 1924, to convalesce from heart trouble. Designed and supervised production of tapestries at Gobelin works in France. Died in Florence, 1928.

BIBLIOGRAPHY: Hartley, Marsden. "The Poetry of Arthur B. Davies' Art," *Touchstone*, vol. VI, no. 5, February 1920, pp. 277–284; Phillips, Duncan. *Arthur B. Davies*. Cambridge, Mass., 1924; Eisen, G. A. "Arthur B. Davies," (obituary) *Art News*, Vol. XXVII, December 1928, p. 12; Cortissoz, Royal. "The Character and Art of Arthur B.

Davies," *Art News*, vol. 27, April 1929, pp. 65–74; Clark, Eliot. "A. B. Davies," *Art in America*, vol. 17, 1929, p. 234–242; Burroughs, Bryson. "Arthur B. Davies," *Arts*, vol. 15, February 1929, pp. 79–93; "Memorial Exhibition of Works of A. B. Davies," catalogue, Metropolitan Museum of Art, February–March 1930, introduction by Bryson Burroughs; Watson, F. "Arthur Bowen Davies," *Magazine of Art*, XLV, December 1952, pp. 362–369; Campbell, L. "An Idealist Who Changed History: Arthur B. Davies," *Art News*, vol. LXI, October 1962, pp. 40–43; Katz, Leslie. "The Originality of Arthur B. Davies," *Arts*, vol. XXXVIII, November 1962, pp. 16–20; "Arthur B. Davies: A Centennial Exhibition," catalogue, Munson-Williams-Proctor Institute, Utica, 1962.

11 *Reluctant Youth*. n.d. *
Oil on canvas, 17 × 22⅛ in. (43.3 × 56.2 cm.).
Signed lower left "A. B. Davies."

Davies constantly reworked his paintings, and rarely dated them. *Reluctant Youth*, probably done prior to 1905, exhibits none of the stylization of his mature pictures.

The treatment of a single figure in a landscape setting has its origins in early 19th century European portraiture, but becomes generalized and poetic through Davies' loose, post-Impressionist rendering. A wistful young girl, isolated from her surroundings, provides allegorical overtones that become increasingly prominent in his later work.

REPRODUCED: *American Art Association Auction Catalogue*, New York, 27 February 1919, no. 50, illus.

12 *Coming Summer*. n.d. *
Oil on canvas, 17⅞ × 30 in. (45.5 × 76.2 cm.).
Signed lower center "A. B. Davies."

Davies' vision is far removed from that of the industrial environment being depicted by his artistic contemporaries. His poetic sensibility, his mysticism and his interest in the eccentricities of past masters (among them Giorgione, Piero di Cosimo, El Greco, and the 19th century Frenchman Puvis de Chavannes) contribute to the eclecticism of *Coming Summer*.

In the seated figure, the discrepancy between her lyrical posture and the curiously dissolving musculature of her torso heralds a stylized cubism prevalent in his later pictures. The second arabesqued, attenuated nude, limbs and drapery floating idyllically before a distant landscape, lends an air of the mysterious and irrational to this painting.

EXHIBITIONS: Marquette University, Milwaukee, Wisconsin, "Festival of American Arts," 20 April–20 May 1956; Ohio Wesleyan University, Delaware, Ohio, 19 November–13 December 1959.

REPRODUCED: *Arts Magazine*, vol. 8, August 1925 (as 'Painting').

13 *Sicily, Flowering Isle*. n.d.
Oil on canvas, 18 × 30⅛ in. (45.7 × 76.5 cm.).
Signed lower left "A. B. Davies."

Charles Demuth (1883–1935)

Born Lancaster, Pennsylvania, 1883. Lame from childhood; diabetes diagnosed in his late 30's; in ill health for remaining fifteen years of his life. Studied at Franklin and Marshall College, Lancaster, 1899; Drexel Institute, Philadelphia, 1901; disliked its emphasis on architecture and applied arts. Studied at Pennsylvania Academy of Fine Arts, 1905, under Thomas Anshutz, Henry McCarter and William Merritt Chase. Travelled to Paris, London and Berlin from about 1907 until 1908. Returned to Pennsylvania Academy in 1908. Second visit to Paris 1912–1914; studied at Académie Moderne, Académie Julian and Académie Colarossi; exposed to Cubism, established friendship with Duchamp. After returning to U.S., he illustrated works of his favorite authors, including Zola, Balzac, Henry James, Poe, and German dramatist Wedekind. First one-man show at Daniel Gallery, 1915; exhibited there to 1925. Spent summer in Provincetown, 1916; winter in Bermuda, 1916–1917, where he began personal adaptation, in water color, of cubist formulas to architectural studies. Summers, 1917, 1918, in Glouster and Lancaster, Pennsylvania. Began using tempera for architectural studies about 1919; oils for industrial scenes about 1920. Third trip to Paris 1921. In group exhibition arranged by Stieglitz at Anderson Galleries, New York, 1925. Early one-man shows: Stieglitz' Intimate Gallery, 1929, An American Place gallery, 1931. Last figure studies done at Provincetown, 1934. Died in Lancaster, Pennsylvania in 1935.

BIBLIOGRAPHY: Gallatin, Albert Eugene. *American Watercolorists*. New York, 1922; Gallatin, A. E. (ed. and intro.). *Charles Demuth*. New York, 1927; Demuth, Charles. "Across a Greco is Written," *Creative Art*, vol. V, no. III, September 1929, pp. 629–34; Murrell, William. *Charles Demuth*. American Artists Group, New York, 1931; Rosenfeld, Paul. "Charles Demuth," *The Nation*, 7 October 1931, pp. 371–373; McBride, Henry. "Charles Demuth, Artist," *Magazine of Art*, XXXL, January 1938, pp. 21–23; McBride, H. "Demuth: Phantoms from Literature," *Art News*, vol. XLIX, March 1950, pp. 18–21; "Charles Demuth," catalogue, Museum of Modern Art, March–June 1950 (introduction by Andrew Carnduff Ritchie); Faison, S. Lane, Jr. "Fact and Art in Charles Demuth's Architectural Pictures," *Magazine*

11 Arthur B. Davies *Reluctant Youth* n.d.

12 Arthur B. Davies *Coming Summer* n.d.

14 Charles Demuth *The Drinkers* 1915

16 Charles Demuth *Poppies* c. 1915

15 Charles Demuth *Dunes* 1915

18 Charles Demuth *Bermuda Landscape* 1916

19 Charles Demuth
The Nut, Pre-Volstead Days 1916

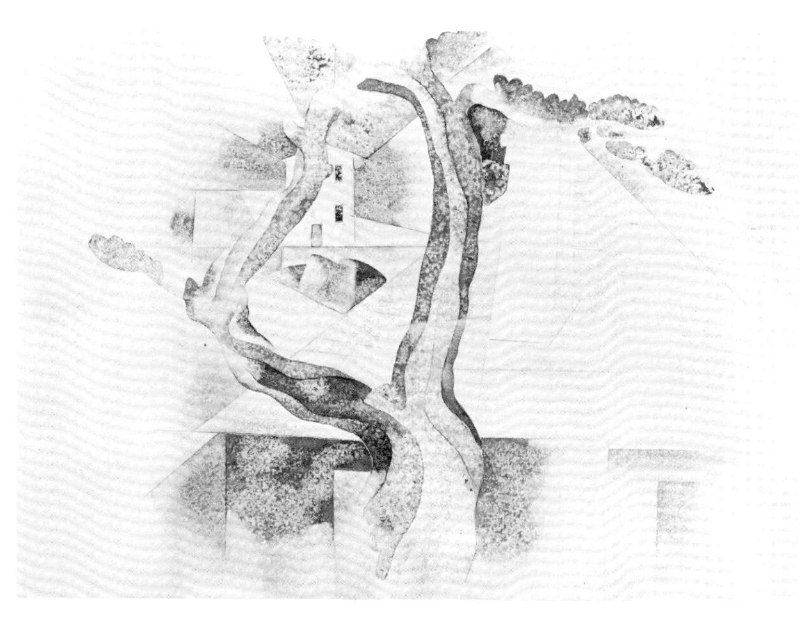

21 Charles Demuth *Trees* c. 1917

20 Charles Demuth *The Circus* 1917

of Art, vol. 43, no. 4, April 1950, pp. 122–128; Smith, Jacob Getlar. "The Water Colors of Charles Demuth," *American Artist*, XLX, May 1955, pp. 26–51; Davidson, A. "Charles Demuth: Stylistic Development," *Bulletin of the Rhode Island School of Design*, March 1968, pp. 9–16.

14 *The Drinkers*. 1915. *

Water color, 10¾ × 8¼ in. (27.3 × 21 cm.).
Signed lower left "C. Demuth."

EXHIBITIONS: Arts Club of Chicago, 1939; Phillips Memorial Gallery, Washington, D.C., "Water Colors and Oil Paintings by Charles Demuth," 3–25 May 1942, no. 30; Dayton Art Institute, Dayton, Ohio, 2 February–4 March 1945; Museum of Modern Art, New York, "Charles Demuth Retrospective Exhibition," 8 March–11 June 1950, circulating exhibition June 1950–June 1951, no. 31; American Federation of Arts, New York, "Adventures in Collecting," October 1958–October 1960, no. 7; Minneapolis Institute of Arts, Minneapolis, Minnesota, "Four Centuries of American Art," 27 November 1963–19 January 1964; William Penn Memorial Museum, Harrisburg, Pennsylvania, "Charles Demuth Exhibition," 24 September–6 November 1966, no. 16; Akron Art Institute, Akron, Ohio, "Charles Demuth Exhibition," 16 April–12 May 1968.

15 *Dunes*. 1915. *

Water color, 11⅜ × 16$\frac{1}{16}$ in. (28.9 × 40.8 cm.).
Signed and dated lower left "C. Demuth 1915."

EXHIBITIONS: Cincinnati Art Museum, 1935; Arts Club of Chicago, 1939; Museum of Modern Art, New York, "Charles Demuth Retrospective Exhibition," 8 March–11 June 1950, circulating exhibition June 1950–June 1951, no. 20, illus. p. 23; Philbrook Art Center, 1956; Allentown Art Museum, Allentown, Pennsylvania, 1–18 April 1961; William Penn Memorial Museum, Harrisburg, Pennsylvania, "Charles Demuth Exhibition," 24 September–6 November 1966, no. 17; Akron Art Institute, Akron, Ohio, "Charles Demuth Exhibition," 16 April–12 May 1968.

16 *Poppies*. c. 1915. *

Water color, 17¾ × 11½ in. (45 × 29.2 cm.).
Signed upper left "C. Demuth."

EXHIBITIONS: Arts Club of Chicago, 1939; Museum of Modern Art, New York, "Charles Demuth Retrospective Exhibition," 8 March–11 June 1950, no. 27; Allentown Art Museum, Allentown, Pennsylvania, 1–18 April 1961; Museum of Fine Arts, St. Petersburg, 1968.

17 *The Primrose*. c. 1915.

Gouache on buff pasteboard, 15¾ × 11$\frac{11}{16}$ in. (40 × 29.7 cm.).

18 *Bermuda Landscape*. 1916. *

Water color, 9¾ × 13$\frac{11}{16}$ in. (24.7 × 34.7 cm.).
Signed and dated lower left" C. Demuth 1916."

EXHIBITIONS: Arts Club of Chicago, 1939; Phillips Memorial Gallery, Washington, D.C., "Water Colors and Oil Paintings by Charles Demuth," 3–25 May 1942, no. 88; Museum of Modern Art, New York, "Charles Demuth Retrospective Exhibition," 8 March–11 June 1950, circulating exhibition, June 1950–June 1951, no. 55; American Federation of Arts, New York, "Adventures in Collecting," October 1958–October 1960, no. 6; Allentown Art Museum, Allentown, Pennsylvania, 1–18 April 1961; Corcoran Gallery, Washington, D.C., "The New Tradition," 27 April–2 June 1963, no. 25, illus. p. 27.

19 *The Nut, Pre-Volstead Days*. 1916. *

Water color, 10$\frac{9}{16}$ × 7$\frac{13}{16}$ in. (26.8 × 19.8 cm.).
Signed and dated lower left "C. Demuth 1916."

EXHIBITIONS: Phillips Memorial Gallery, Washington, D.C., "Water Colors and Oil Paintings by Charles Demuth," 3–25 May 1942, no. 22; Dayton Art Institute, Dayton, Ohio, 2 February–4 March 1945; Museum of Modern Art, New York, "Charles Demuth Retrospective Exhibition," 8 March–11 June 1950, no. 51; Philbrook Art Center, 1956; William Penn Memorial Museum, Harrisburg, Pennsylvania, "Charles Demuth Exhibition," 24 September–6 November 1966, no. 43; Akron Art Institute, Akron, Ohio, "Charles Demuth Exhibition," 16 April–12 May 1968.

20 *The Circus*. 1917. *

Water color, 8 × 10⅝ in. (20.4 × 27 cm.).
Signed and dated lower left "C. Demuth 1917."

Between 1917 and 1919, Demuth executed a series of pictures depicting circus and vaudeville entertainers, a theme which he abandoned shortly afterwards. By concentrating on the physical rather than psychological characteristics of the performers, he integrated style and subject matter. Thin watercolor washes and an energetic, rythmic line provide a counterpart to the dexterity and weightlessness of the acrobats. Compositionally, Demuth further accentuated their precarious stance by means of a high vantage point and horizontal and diagonal forms which sweep across the surface of the picture.

EXHIBITIONS: Cleveland Museum of Art, Cleveland, Ohio, "American Painting From 1860 Until Today," 23 June–4 October 1937, no. 43, plate 28; Whitney Museum, New York, "Demuth Memorial Exhibition," 15 December 1937–16 January 1938, no. 69, illus.; Museum of Modern Art, New York, "Tenth Anniversary Exhibition: Art in Our Time," May–October 1939, no. 215, illus.; Phillips Memorial Gallery, Washington, D.C., "Water Colors and Oil Paintings by Charles Demuth," 3–25 May 1942, no. 46; Dayton Art Institute, Dayton, Ohio, 2 February–4 March 1945; National Gallery of Fine Art, Inter-American Office, Washington, D.C. (prepared by the Walker Art Center, Minneapolis, Minnesota), "A Survey of Water Color—U.S.A., from 1870–1946," circulating exhibit to Central and South America, 1946, no. 37, illus. p. 34; American Federation of Arts, New York, "Early Twentieth Century American Water Colors," circulating exhibition, 1 August 1948–1 June 1949; Albertina Gallery, Vienna, "Amerikanische Meister des Aquareils," Autumn 1949, no. 20; Museum of Modern Art, New York, "Charles Demuth Retrospective Exhibition," 8 March–11 June 1950, no. 68, illus. p. 35; Carnegie Institute, 1952; Philbrook Art Center, 1956; Albany Institute, 1958; American Federation of Arts, New York, "Adventures in Collecting," October 1958–October 1960; Milwaukee Art Center, Milwaukee, Wisconsin, "Ten Americans," 21 September–5 November 1961, no. 8; Whitney Museum, New York, "The Decade of the Armory Show, New Directions in American Art, 1910–1920," 27 February–14 April 1963, no. 25, illus. p. 23; Whitney Museum, New York, "Art of the United States," 27 September–27 November 1966, no. 66.

REPRODUCED: *Art Digest*, January 1938, p. 5; Ritchie, Andrew Carnduff. "Charles Demuth," *Magazine of Art*, vol. 1, no. 8, May 1946.

21 *Trees*. c. 1917. *

Water color, $9\frac{11}{16} \times 13\frac{11}{16}$ in. (24.6×34.8 cm.).
Signed lower left "C. Demuth."

EXHIBITIONS: Whitney Museum, New York, "Demuth Memorial Exhibition," 15 December 1937–16 January 1938, no. 78; Phillips Memorial Gallery, Washington, D.C., "Water Colors and Oil Paintings by Charles Demuth," 3–25 May 1942, no. 24; Dayton Art Institute, Dayton, Ohio, 2 February–4 March 1945; American Federation of Arts, New York, "Early Twentieth Century American Water Colors," circulating exhibition, 1 August 1948–1 June 1949; Albertina Gallery, Vienna, "Amerikanische Meister des Aquarells," Autumn 1949, no. 19; Museum of Modern Art, New York, "Charles Demuth Retrospective Exhibition," 8 March–11 June 1950, circulating exhibition June 1950–June 1951, no. 61.

REPRODUCED: Brown, Milton. *American Painting from the Armory Show to the Depression*. Princeton, 1955, p. 114.

22 *Landscape*. n.d.

Water color, $9\frac{11}{16} \times 13\frac{5}{8}$ in. (24.6×34.6 cm.).
Signed lower left "C. Demuth."

23 *Houses*. 1918. *

Water color, $13\frac{3}{4} \times 9\frac{3}{4}$ in. (34.9×24.8 cm.).
Signed and dated lower left "C. Demuth 1918."

EXHIBITIONS: Arts Club of Chicago, 1939, no. 6; Phillips Memorial Gallery, Washington, D.C., "Water Colors and Oil Paintings by Charles Demuth," 3–25 May 1942, no. 28; Dayton Art Institute, Dayton, Ohio, 2 February–4 March 1945; Norton Gallery of Art, West Palm Beach, Florida, "Masters of Water Color—Marin, Demuth and Prendergast," 3–26 February 1950, no. 12; Museum of Modern Art, New York, "Charles Demuth Retrospective Exhibition," 8 March–11 June 1950, circulating exhibition, June 1950–June 1951, no. 73; Philbrook Art Center, 1956; Albany Institute, 1958; American Federation of Arts, New York, "Adventures in Collecting," October 1958–October 1960, no. 4; Allentown Art Museum, Allentown, Pennsylvania, 1–18 April 1961.

REPRODUCED: Soby, James Thrall. *Contemporary Painters*. Museum of Modern Art, New York, 1948, p. 13.

24 *Housetops*. 1918. *

Water color, $9\frac{3}{4} \times 13\frac{11}{16}$ in. (24.8×34.8 cm.).
Signed and dated lower left "C. Demuth 1918."

EXHIBITIONS: Little Gallery of Contemporary Art, Philadelphia, Pennsylvania, October 1932; Whitney Museum, New York, "Demuth Memorial Show," 15 December 1937–16 January 1938, no. 17; Arts Club of Chicago, 1939, no. 5; Phillips Memorial Gallery, Washington, D.C., "Water Colors and Oil Paintings by Charles Demuth," 3–25 May 1942, no. 44; Dayton Art Institute, Dayton, Ohio, 2 February–4 March 1945; Stedelijk Museum, Amsterdam, 15 June–15 September 1950; Philbrook Art Center, 1956; Akron Art Institute, Akron, Ohio, "Charles Demuth Exhibition," 16 April–12 May 1968.

REPRODUCED: Davidson, Martha. "Demuth, Architect of Painting," *Art News*, 18 December 1937, p. 8; *Art News Annual*, XVIII, 1948, p. 36.

25 *Columbia*. 1919. *

Water color, $11\frac{15}{16} \times 8$ in. (28.8×20.3 cm.).
Signed and dated lower left "C. Demuth 1919."

EXHIBITIONS: Whitney Museum, New York, "Demuth Memorial Exhibition," 15 December 1937–16 January 1938, no. 7; Phillips Memorial Gallery, Washington, D.C., "Water Colors and Oil Paintings by Charles Demuth," 3–25 May 1942, no. 37; Museum of Modern Art, New York, "Art in Progress," 24 May–15 October 1944; Tate Gallery, London, "American Painting from the Eighteenth Century to the Present Day," June–July 1946, no. 57; Norton Gallery of Art, West Palm Beach, Florida, "Masters of Water Color—Marin, Demuth and Prendergast," 3–26 February 1950, no. 13; Museum of Modern Art, New York, "Charles Demuth Retrospective Exhibition," 8 March–11 June 1950, circulating exhibition June 1950–June 1951, no. 98; William Penn Memorial Museum, Harrisburg, Pennsylvania, "Charles Demuth Exhibition," 24 September–6 November 1966, no. 76; Akron Art Institute, Akron, Ohio, "Charles Demuth Exhibition," 16 April–12 May 1968.

REPRODUCED: Watson, Forbes. "American Collections—The Ferdinand Howald Collection," *Arts*, vol. 8, August 1925, p. 87; Gallatin, A. E. *Charles Demuth*. New York, 1927; Murrell, William. *Charles Demuth*. American Artists Group, New York, 1931, p. 45; *L'Amour d'Art*, vol. 4, December 1932, p. 764.

26 *Flowers*. 1919. *
Water color, 13¾ × 9 11/16 in. (34.9 × 24.6 cm.).
Monogram and dated lower right "C. D. 1919."

Throughout his career, Demuth executed studies of fruit and flowers whose lyricism and precise draughtsmanship are unsurpassed. The picture contains a residual Cubist analysis of forms, here compressed against a large expanse of white paper. Crisp, elegant and cool, Demuth's interpretation of organic forms was a radical departure from conventional still-life prototypes.

EXHIBITIONS: Cleveland Museum of Art, Cleveland, Ohio, "American Painting From 1860 Until Today," 23 June–4 October 1937, no. 44; Whitney Museum, New York, "Demuth Memorial Exhibition," 15 December 1937–16 January 1938, no. 61; The Arts Club of Chicago, 1939, no. 8; Phillips Memorial Gallery, Washington, D.C., "Water Colors and Oil Paintings by Charles Demuth," 3–25 May 1942, no. 34; Dayton Art Institute, Dayton, Ohio, 2 February–4 March 1945; American Federation of Arts, New York, "Early Twentieth Century American Water Colors," circulating exhibition, 1 August 1948–1 June 1949; Museum of Modern Art, New York, "Charles Demuth Retrospective Exhibition," 8 March–11 June 1950, circulating exhibition, June 1950–June 1951, no. 97; Carnegie Institute, 1952; Philbrook Art Center, 1956.

REPRODUCED: *Magazine of Art*, January 1938, p. 21.

27 *Cottage Window*. 1919.
Gouache on pasteboard, 15⅜ × 11 5/16 in. (38 × 28.7 cm.).
Signed on back "Charles Demuth."

28 *The Tower*. 1920. *
(Original title: *Tower—After Sir Christopher Wren*).
Tempera on pasteboard, 23 × 19 7/16 in. (58.7 × 49.4 cm.).

One of his best-known pictures, *The Tower* marks a turning point in Demuth's style. It heralds a new interest in urban American environment, rendered in the geometric, planar mode of a Precisionist vocabulary.

The original title indicates that Demuth wryly acknowledged the 1920s' attempt to break ties with European art by establishing a native American tradition and style. A colonial church tower is presented as the American counterpart to St. Paul's Cathedral, London, built in the late 17th century by the famous English architect Sir Christopher Wren.

EXHIBITIONS: Smith College Museum of Art, Northampton, Massachusetts, "Five Americans," 19 May–19 June 1934, no. 13; Cleveland Museum of Art, Cleveland, Ohio, "American Painting from 1860 Until Today," 23 June–4 October 1937, no. 42; Whitney Museum, New York, "Demuth Memorial Exhibition," 15 December 1937–16 January 1938, no. 42; Modern Art Society, Cincinnati, Ohio, "A New Realism," 12 March–7 April 1941, no. 17; Phillips Memorial Gallery, Washington, D.C., "Water Colors and Oil Paintings by Charles Demuth," 3–25 May 1942, no. 50; Tate Gallery, London, "American Painting from the Eighteenth Century to the Present Day," June–July 1946, no. 60; Albertina Gallery, Vienna, "Amerikanische Meister des Aquarells," Autumn 1949, no. 24; Museum of Modern Art, New York, "Charles Demuth Retrospective Exhibition," 8 March–11 June 1950, circulating exhibition, June 1950–June 1951, no. 104; Carnegie Institute, 1952; Walker Art Center, 1960; William Penn Memorial Museum, Harrisburg, Pennsylvania, "Charles Demuth Exhibition," 24 September–6 November 1966, no. 83, illus.

REPRODUCED: *Dial*, February 1921, vol. 70, p. 125; Kootz, Samuel M. *Modern American Painters*. New York, 1930, plate 8; Murrell, William. *Charles Demuth*. American Artists Group, New York, 1931, p. 31; Lane, James W. *Masters in Modern Art*. Boston, 1936, p. 86; *Parnassus*, IX, December 1937 (College Art Association, New York), p. 2.

29 *Modern Conveniences*. 1921. *
Oil on canvas, 25 7/16 × 20 15/16 in. (64.6 × 53.2 cm.).
Signed and dated lower left "C. Demuth 1921."

The ironic implications of Demuth's titles derive in part from his friendship with Marcel Duchamp, whom he had met in Paris. By 1915, with Duchamp, Picabia and Man Ray all living in New York, the Dada movement had spread to America.

In this painting, Demuth retains the spontaneity of his watercolor technique. Mundane shapes are rendered with delicate linearity, creating a pictorial as well as verbal paradox.

EXHIBITIONS: Brooklyn Museum, New York, "International Exhibition of Modern Art" (organized by the Société Anonyme), 19 November–20 December 1926, no. 236; Museum of Modern Art, New York, "Paintings by Nineteen Living Americans," 13 December 1929–12 January 1930, no. 11; Smith College Museum of Art, Northampton, Massachusetts, "Five Americans," 19 May–19 June 1934; Cincinnati Art Museum, 1935; Whitney Museum, New York, "Demuth Memorial Exhibition," 15 December 1937–16 January 1938, no. 16; Modern Art Society, Cincinnati, Ohio, "A New Realism," 12 March–7 April 1941, no. 14; Phillips Memorial Gallery, Washington, D.C., "Water Colors and Oil Paintings by Charles Demuth," 3–25 May 1942, no. 47; Whitney Museum, New York, "Pioneers of Modern Art," 9 April–19 May 1946, circulated by American Federation of Arts, 1946–1947, no. 31; Corcoran Gallery, Washington, D.C., "De gustibus, An Exhibition of American Paintings," 7 January–20 February 1949, no. 45, illus.; Museum of Modern Art, New York, "Charles Demuth Retrospective Exhibition," 8 March–11

June 1950, circulating exhibition, June 1950–June 1951, no. 113; Smith College Museum of Art, Northampton, Massachusetts, 15 May–15 November 1951; Norfolk Museum, Norfolk, Virginia, "Significant American Moderns," March–April 1953, illus.; Wildenstein Galleries, New York, "American and French Modern Masters" (organized by La Napoule Art Foundation, New York), 4–28 May 1955, no. 7; Davison Art Center, Wesleyan University, Middletown, Connecticut, "America Seen," 15 September–10 October 1957; Walker Art Center, 1960; Whitney Museum, New York, "The Decade of the Armory Show, New Directions in American Art, 1910–1920," 27 February–14 April 1963, no. 27, illus. p. 49; Indiana University Museum of Art, Bloomington, Indiana, "American Painting, 1910–1960," 19 April–10 May 1964, no. 18, illus.; American Federation of Arts, New York, "Realism and Reality," January 1965–January 1966, no. 14; Whitney Museum, New York, "Art of the United States," 27 September–27 November 1966, no. 68.

REPRODUCED: *Arts*, vol. 3, January 1923, p. 75; Kootz, Samuel M. *Modern American Painters*. New York, 1930, plate 6; Murrell, William. *Charles Demuth*. American Artists Group, New York, 1931, p. 33; *Art News*, 18 December 1931, p. 7; *see:* Faison, S. Lane, Jr. "Fact and Art in Charles Demuth's Architectural Pictures," *Magazine of Art*, vol. 43, no. 4, April 1950, p. 125.

30 *Incense of a New Church*. 1921. *
Oil on canvas, 25½ × 19¹³⁄₁₆ in. (64.8 × 50.3 cm.).
Signed and dated on back "C. Demuth Lancaster, Pa. 1921."

Demuth's fascination with machinery and the structures of urbanism was expressed not in terms of protest, but of personal poetry. Looming smokestacks and waste fumes are treated as harbingers of their own veneration. Thus Demuth ironically questions his own poetic attitude toward the changing values wrought by the Machine Age.

EXHIBITIONS: Cincinnati Art Museum, 1935; Whitney Museum, New York, "Demuth Memorial Exhibition," 15 December 1937–16 January 1938, no. 95; Modern Art Society, Cincinnati, Ohio, "A New Realism," 12 March–7 April, 1941, no. 13; Phillips Memorial Gallery, Washington, D.C., "Water Colors and Oil Paintings by Charles Demuth," 3–25 May 1942, no. 52; Whitney Museum, New York, "Pioneers of Modern Art in America," 19 April–19 May 1946, circulated by American Federation of Arts, 1946–1947, no. 30, illus.; Museum of Modern Art, New York, "Charles Demuth Retrospective Exhibition," 8 March–11 June 1950, circulating exhibition, June 1950–June 1951, no. 114; Whitney Museum, New York, "The Decade of the Armory Show, New Directions in American Art 1910–1920," 27 February–14 April 1963, no. 26a; Corcoran Gallery, Washington, D.C., "The New Tradition," 27 April–2 June 1963, no. 27, illus. p. 36; Gallery of Modern Art, New York, "The Twenties Revisited," 29 June–6 September 1965; Smithsonian Institution, Washington, D.C., "Roots of Abstract Art in America, 1910–1930," 1 December 1965–16 January 1966, no. 28, illus.; William Penn Memorial Museum, Harrisburg, Pennsylvania, "Charles Demuth Exhibition," 24 September–6 November 1966, no. 86; University of New Mexico Art Museum, 1967; Museum of Modern Art, New York, "The Machine," 27 November 1968–9 February 1969.

REPRODUCED: Brown, Milton. *American Painting from the Armory Show to the Depression*. Princeton, 1955, p. 115; "The Quest of Charles Sheeler," catalogue, University of Iowa, 1963, p. 39; Rose, Barbara. "How to Murder an Avant Garde," *Art Forum*, vol. 4, no. 3, November 1965, p. 30; Rose, Barbara. *American Art Since 1900*. New York, 1967, p. 106.

31 *Aucassin and Nicolette*. 1921. *
Oil on canvas, 23⁹⁄₁₆ × 19½ in. (59.8 × 49.5 cm.).
Signed and dated on back "C. Demuth 1921."

Aucassin and Nicolette were the persecuted lovers of a medieval French romance. The anthropomorphic quality of two towers, huddled together under a bleak sky, undoubtedly prompted Demuth's reference to the fable. A. E. Gallatin, in 1927, recalled "with great satisfaction the uproar and indignation this title caused in academic circles."

EXHIBITIONS: Cincinnati Art Museum, 1935; Whitney Museum, New York, "Demuth Memorial Exhibition," 15 December 1937–16 January 1938, no. 86; Modern Art Society, Cincinnati, Ohio, "A New Realism," 12 March–7 April 1941, no. 11; Phillips Memorial Gallery, Washington, D.C., "Water Colors and Oil Paintings By Charles Demuth," 3–25 May 1942; American Federation of Arts, New York, December 1949–November 1950; Carnegie Institute, 1952; American Federation of Arts, New York, "American Impressionists: Two Generations," October 1963–May 1965; Public Education Association, New York, "Seven Decades of Modern Art, 1895–1965," 26 April–21 May 1966, no. 133, illus. p. 80; William Penn Memorial Museum, Harrisburg, Pennsylvania, "Charles Demuth Exhibition," 24 September–6 November 1966, no. 84; Akron Art Institute, Akron, Ohio, "Charles Demuth Exhibition," 16 April–12 May 1968.

REPRODUCED: *Arts*, vol. 3, January 1923, p. 76; *Magazine of Art*, vol. 43, no. 4, April 1950, p. 125; *see:* Faison, S. Lane, Jr. "Fact and Art in Charles Demuth's Architectural Pictures," pp. 124–125.

32 *Zinnia and Snapdragons*. c. 1921. *
Water color, 9⅝ × 12¹¹⁄₁₆ in. (24.4 × 32.2 cm.).

EXHIBITIONS: Phillips Memorial Gallery, Washington, D.C., "Water Colors and Oil Paintings by Charles Demuth," 3–25 May 1942, no. 14; Allentown Art Museum, Allentown, Pennsylvania, 1–18 April 1961; Museum of Fine Arts, St. Petersburg, 1968.

26 Charles Demuth *Flowers* 1919

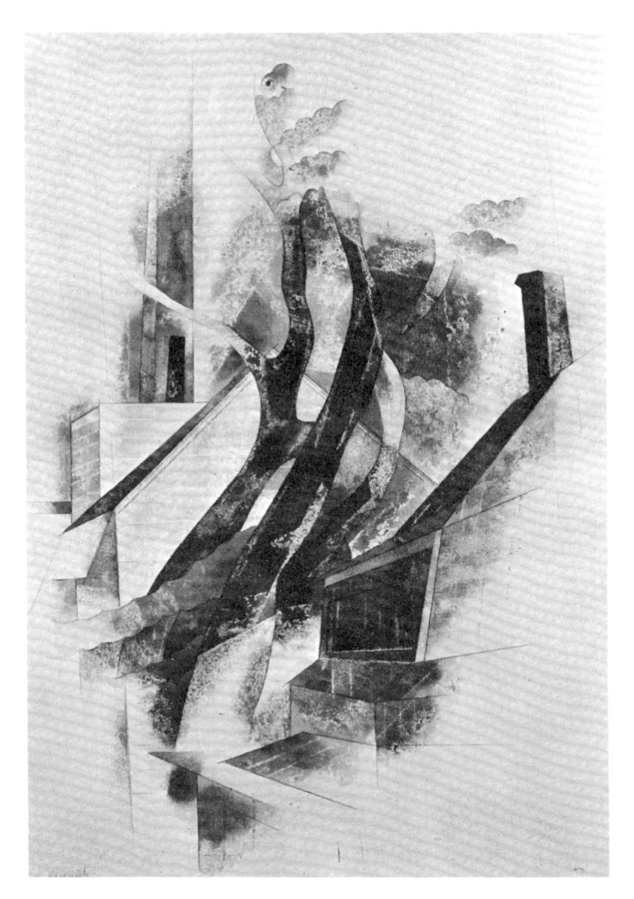

23 Charles Demuth *Houses* 1918

25 Charles Demuth *Columbia* 1919

24 Charles Demuth *Housetops* 1918

28 Charles Demuth *The Tower* 1920

29 Charles Demuth *Modern Conveniences* 1921

30 Charles Demuth *Incense of a New Church* 1921

31 Charles Demuth *Aucassin and Nicolette* 1921

32 Charles Demuth *Zinnia and Snapdragons* c. 1921

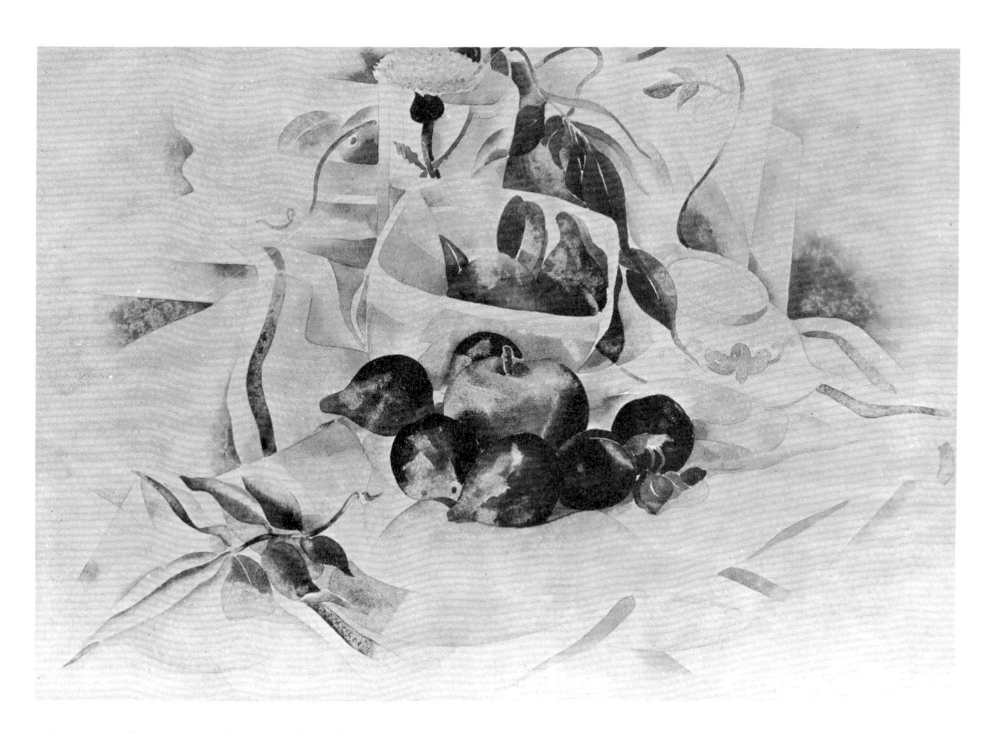

34 Charles Demuth *Still Life No.* 1 c. 1922

33 Charles Demuth *Paquebot Paris* c. 1921

35 Charles Demuth *Still Life No.* 2 1922

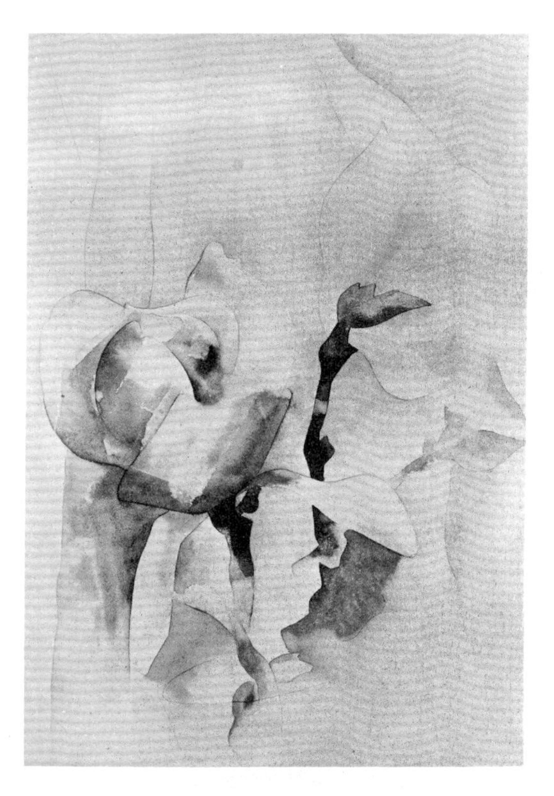

36 Charles Demuth *Still Life No.* 3 1922

37 Charles Demuth *Fruit No.* 1 1922

33 *Paquebot Paris*. c. 1921. *
Oil on canvas, 24½ × 19⁷⁄₁₆ in. (62.2 × 49.4 cm.).

In 1921 Demuth made his third visit to France, travelling on the steamship *Paris*. Two pencil sketches for this painting, dated August of that year, are reproduced in Andrew Ritchie's *Demuth* catalogue (Museum of Modern Art, N.Y., 1950, p. 75), although it is possible that the painting itself may have been executed several years later.

The simplified structural analysis of *Paquebot* closely resembles that of Sheeler's *Upper Deck*, 1929, (Fogg Museum), which may have been influenced by the Demuth work.

EXHIBITIONS: Brooklyn Museum, New York, "International Exhibition of Modern Art" (organized by the Société Anonyme), 19 November–20 December 1926, no. 237; Museum of Modern Art, New York, "Paintings by Nineteen Living Americans," 13 December 1929–12 January 1930, no. 12; Whitney Museum, New York, "Demuth Memorial Exhibition," 15 December 1937–16 January 1938, no. 1; Modern Art Society, Cincinnati, Ohio, "A New Realism," 12 March–7 April 1941, no. 16, illus. p. 7; Phillips Memorial Gallery, Washington, D.C., "Water Colors and Oil Paintings by Charles Demuth," 3–25 May 1942, no. 56; Museum of Modern Art, New York, "Charles Demuth Retrospective Exhibition," 8 March–11 June, 1950, circulating exhibition June 1950–June 1951, no. 118, illus. p. 74; Brooklyn Museum, New York, "Revolution and Tradition," 15 November 1951–6 January 1952, no. 41, illus. no. 72; Carnegie Institute, 1952; American Federation of Arts, New York, "Landmarks in American Art," 26 February–28 March 1953, no. 45, illus. no. 45; Contemporary Arts Center of Cincinnati Art Museum and Dayton Art Institute, Ohio, "An American Viewpoint: Realism in the Twentieth Century," 10 October 1957–15 January 1958, illus.; Walker Art Center, 1960; American Federation of Arts, New York, "Magic Realism—What it Is," March 1964–March 1965; Smithsonian Institution, Washington, D.C., "Roots of Abstract Art in America 1910–1930," 1 December 1965–16 January 1966, no. 22; William Penn Memorial Museum, Harrisburg, Pennsylvania, "Charles Demuth Memorial Exhibition," 24 September–6 November 1966, no. 88; American Federation of Arts, New York, "From Synchromism Forward: A View of Abstract Art in America," circulating exhibition, November 1967–November 1968.

REPRODUCED: Gallatin, Albert E. *Charles Demuth*. New York, 1927; Kootz, Samuel M. *Modern American Painters*. New York, 1930, plate 7; Murrell, William. *Charles Demuth*. American Artists Group, New York, 1931, p. 47; Baur, John I. H. *Revolution and Tradition in Modern American Art*. Boston, 1951, illus. no. 72; Brown, Milton. *American Painting from the Armory Show to the Depression*. Princeton, 1955, p. 119; Pierson, William H., Jr., and Martha Davidson, (eds.). *Arts of the U.S., A Pictorial Survey*. New York, 1960, no. 3073, illus. p. 338.

34 *Still Life No. 1*. c. 1922. *
Water color, 11¾ × 17¾ in. (29.8 × 45.8 cm.).

EXHIBITIONS: Museum of Modern Art, New York, "Paintings by Nineteen Living Americans," 13 December 1929–12 January 1930, no. 10, p. 16; Smith College Museum of Art, Northampton, Massachusetts. "Five Americans," 19 May–19 June, 1934, no. 15; Cleveland Museum of Art, Cleveland, Ohio, "American Painting from 1860 Until Today," 23 June–4 October, 1937, no. 47; Whitney Museum, New York, "Demuth Memorial Exhibition," 15 December 1937–16 January 1938, no. 62; Arts Club of Chicago, 1939, no. 10; Phillips Memorial Gallery, Washington, D.C., "Water Colors and Oil Paintings by Charles Demuth," 3–25 May 1942, no. 1; Dayton Art Institute, Dayton, Ohio, 2 February–4 March, 1945; Museum of Modern Art, New York, "Charles, Demuth Retrospective Exhibition," 8 March–11 June 1950, circulating exhibition, June 1950–June 1951, no. 120; Carnegie Institute, 1952; American Federation of Arts, "American Still Life Painting 1913–1967," circulating exhibition, October 1967–October 1968.

REPRODUCED: Watson, Forbes. "The Ferdinand Howald Collection," *Arts*, vol. 8, August 1925, p. 94; Mather, Frank J., Jr., and William J. Henderson. *The Pageant of America, the American Spirit in Art*. vol. 12, New Haven, 1927, pl. 65; Gallatin, A. E. *Charles Demuth*. New York, 1927, plate 24; Murrell, William, *Charles Demuth*. American Artists Group, New York, 1931, p. 27.

35 *Still Life, No. 2*. 1922. *
Water color and ink, 9⁹⁄₁₆ × 12⅝ in. (24.3 × 32 cm.).
Signed and dated lower right "C. Demuth 1922."

EXHIBITIONS: Phillips Memorial Gallery, Washington, D.C., "Water Colors and Oil Paintings by Charles Demuth," 3–25 May 1942, no. 8; Museum of Modern Art, New York, "Charles Demuth Retrospective Exhibition," 8 March–11 June 1950, circulating exhibition, June 1950–June 1951, no. 121, illus. p. 76; Philbrook Art Center, 1956; American Federation of Arts, New York, "Adventures in Collecting," October 1958–October 1960, no. 8; William Penn Memorial Museum, Harrisburg, Pennsylvania, "Charles Demuth Exhibition," 24 September–6 November 1966, no. 91; Akron Art Institute, Akron, Ohio, "Charles Demuth Exhibition," 16 April–12 May 1968.

36 *Still Life, No. 3*. 1922. *
Water color, 13½ × 9⅝ in. (34.2 × 24.4 cm.).

EXHIBITIONS: Phillips Memorial Gallery, Washington, D.C., "Water Colors and Oil Paintings by Charles Demuth," 3–25 May 1942, no. 43; Museum of Modern Art, New York, "Charles Demuth Retrospective Exhibition," 8 March–11 June 1950, circulating exhibition, June 1950–June 1951, no. 122; Carnegie Institute, 1952; Philbrook Art Center, 1956;

Albany Institute, 1958; American Federation of Arts, New York, "Adventures in Collecting," October 1958–October 1960, no. 3; Museum of Fine Arts, St. Petersburg, 1968.

37 *Fruit No. 1*. 1922. *
Water color, 9⁵⁄₁₆ × 12¹³⁄₁₆ in. (23.6 × 32.6 cm.).
Signed and dated lower center "C. Demuth 1922."

EXHIBITIONS: Phillips Memorial Gallery, Washington, D.C., "Water Colors and Oil Paintings by Charles Demuth," 3–25 May 1942, no. 12; Dayton Art Institute, Dayton, Ohio, 2 February–4 March 1945; Allentown Art Museum, Allentown, Pennsylvania, 1–18 April 1961; Museum of Fine Arts, St. Petersburg, 1968.

38 *Fruit No. 2*. 1922.
Water color, 9⅜ × 12¹⁵⁄₁₆ in. (23.8 × 32.9 cm.).
Signed and dated lower right "C. Demuth 1922."

39 *California Tomatoes*. c. 1923.
Water color, 11½ × 13¹¹⁄₁₆ in. (29.2 × 34.8 cm.).

40 *Pears*. 1924.
Water color, 11¾ × 17¹¹⁄₁₆ in. (29.9 × 45 cm.).
Signed and dated lower right "C. Demuth, 1924, Lancaster."

41 *Bowl of Oranges*. 1925.
Water color, 13⁷⁄₁₆ × 19³⁄₁₆ in. (34.2 × 50.3 cm.).

Preston Dickinson (1891–1930)

Born New York City, 1891. Few biographical facts known. Studied at Art Students League under Ernest Lawson, Bellows and Bridgeman around 1910. Went to Paris sometime between 1911 and 1912 to study old masters in the Louvre. Exhibited in *Salon des Artistes Français*, 1912. Influenced significantly by works of Cézanne; engaged in close study of Japanese print techniques in 1913 while still in Paris. First one-man show at Daniel Gallery, New York, 1924. Three subsequent shows there in 1927, 1930 and 1932. Belonged at one time to the Society of Independent Artists and to the Whitney Studio Club in 1925. Travelled frequently in Canada. One-man exhibition in Quebec, 1926–1927. Returned to Europe in 1930 to find an inexpensive place to live and paint. Died in small Spanish town near the French border in 1930 at the age of 39.

BIBLIOGRAPHY: Watson, Forbes. "Preston Dickinson," *The Arts*, vol. 5, May 1924, pp. 284–288; Kootz, Samuel M. *Modern American Painters*. New York, 1930, pp. 34–35; Brown, Milton W. "Cubist Realism: An American Style," *Marsyas*, New York University Institute of Fine Arts, 1943–1945, pp. 139–160.

42 *A Bridge*. 1918.
Oil on canvas, 20 × 26 in. (50.7 × 66 cm.).
Signed and dated lower right "P. Dickinson '18."

43 *Hillside*. 1919. *
Water color, 16¾ × 11³⁄₁₆ in. (42.6 × 28.4 cm.).
Signed and dated lower right "P. Dickinson '19."

EXHIBITIONS: Whitney Museum, New York, "Pioneers of Modern Art in America," 9 April–19 May 1946, no. 35, circulated by American Federation of Arts, 1946–1947; Philbrook Art Center, 1956; Walker Art Center, 1960.

44 *Women Bathing*. n.d. *
Water color, 17³⁄₁₆ × 13½ in. (43.5 × 34.3 cm.).
Signed lower right "P. Dickinson."

EXHIBITIONS: John Herron Art Institute, Indianapolis, Indiana, "Water Colors by American Artists," 1 February–8 March 1944; Indiana University, Bloomington, Indiana, 10–25 March 1944; Allentown Art Museum, Allentown, Pennsylvania, 1–18 April 1961.

45 *Man Reading*. n.d.
Water color, 14¾ × 10¾ in. (37.5 × 27.3 cm.).
Signed lower right "P. Dickinson."

46 *The Absinthe Drinker*. c. 1921.
Water color, 10¹³⁄₁₆ × 11⅝ in. (27.5 × 29.5 cm.).
Signed lower left "P. Dickinson."

47 *Interior*. n.d.
Oil on canvas, 24⅛ × 20 in. (61.2 × 50.7 cm.).
Signed lower right "P. Dickinson."

48 *Landscape*. n.d. *
Oil on canvas, 25⅛ × 30 in. (63.8 × 76.2 cm.).

The Cézanne paintings that Dickinson saw in New York's 1913 Armory show were to affect his landscapes even more than his still lifes. Buildings and trees seem to materialize of their own volition from the surrounding space, but unlike Cézanne, the picture surface here remains essentially flat and decorative. Despite Dickinson's intellectual bias, such landscapes reveal a poetic rather than analytic use of color, creating a fluctuating, dreamy ambience.

EXHIBITIONS: Cincinnati Art Museum, 1935; American Federation of Arts, New York, "Pioneers of Modern Art in America," circulating exhibition 1946–1947; Carnegie Institute, 1952.

REPRODUCED: *Arts*, vol.8, August 1925, p. 71; *Formes*, no. 21, January 1932, p. 204a; Museum of Modern Art, Art in Embassies program, New Delhi (1), SPICE 23–59, 1961–1964.

43 Preston Dickinson *Hillside* 1919

44 Preston Dickinson *Women Bathing* n.d.

48 Preston Dickinson *Landscape* n.d.

49 Preston Dickinson *The Black House* c. 1923

55 Preston Dickinson *Still Life No. 2* n.d.

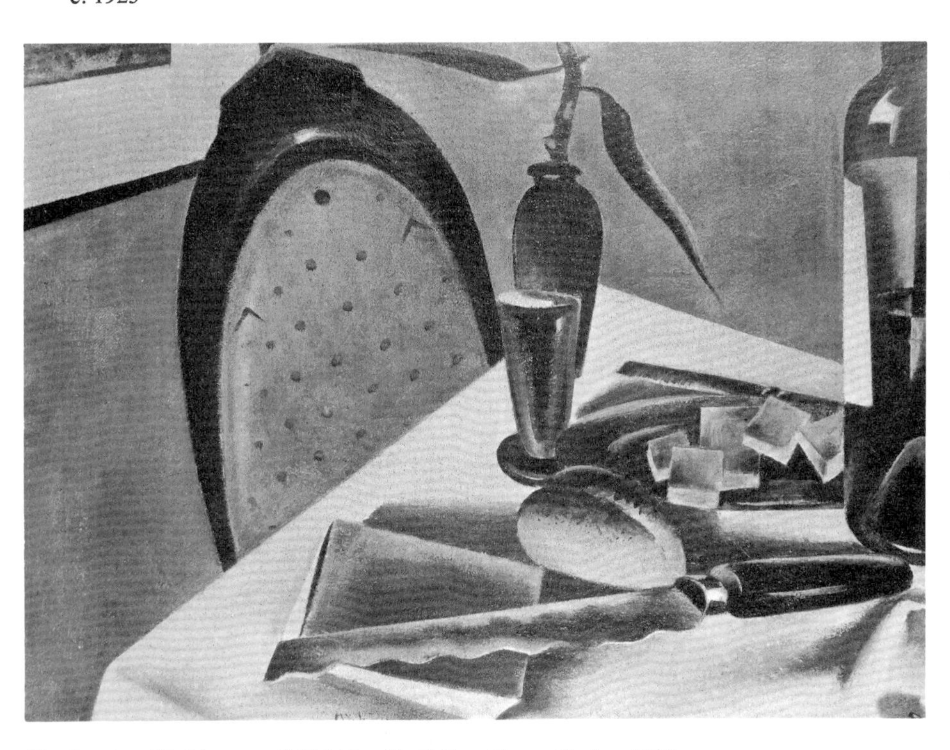

58 Preston Dickinson *Still Life with Yellow Green Chair* 1928

50 Preston Dickinson *Factories* 1924

53 Preston Dickinson *Grain Elevators* 1924

49 *The Black House.* c. 1923. *
Water color and pastel, 16¾ × 10¾ in. (42.5 × 27.3 cm.).
Signed center right side "P. Dickinson."

EXHIBITIONS: Arts Club of Chicago, 1939, no. 13; University Gallery, University of Minnesota, Minneapolis, Minnesota, December 1942; John Herron Art Institute, Indianapolis, Indiana, "Water Colors by American Artists," 1 February–8 March 1944; Indiana University Museum of Art, Bloomington, Indiana, 10–25 March 1944; Allen Memorial Art Museum, Oberlin College, Oberlin, Ohio, 20 November 1950–10 September 1951; Albany Institute, 1958; American Federation of Arts, New York, "Adventures in Collecting," October 1958–October 1960, no. 12; Museum of Fine Arts, St. Petersburg, 1968.

50 *Factories.* 1924. *
Oil on canvas, 29⅞ × 25¼ in. (75.8 × 64 cm.).
Signed and dated lower right "P. Dickinson '24."

Dickinson's "Cubist-Realism" differed from that of his contemporaries; he preferred to treat natural or industrial landscapes in a decorative manner, rather than to simplify them by the elimination of detail. The delicate fragmentation of solid shapes is similar to the calligraphic style of Oriental prints, which Dickinson greatly admired. Such diffracted, active volumes do not have the ominous presence found in similar depictions by Sheeler, Demuth or Niles Spencer.

EXHIBITIONS: Daniel Gallery, New York, "Paintings and Drawings by Preston Dickinson," March 1924, no. 1; Cincinnati Art Museum, Cincinnati, Ohio, "36th Annual Exhibition of American Art," 31 May–30 June 1929, illus.; Knoedler Galleries, New York, "Preston Dickinson Exhibition of Paintings," February 1943, no. 25; Walker Art Center, 1960; Peale House of the Pennsylvania Academy of the Fine Arts, Philadelphia, Pennsylvania," Early Moderns Exhibition," 31 January–3 March 1968.
REPRODUCED: *Arts*, vol. 5, May 1924, p. 288.

51 *Bridge Over River.* n.d.
Pastel, 16¼ × 10⅝ in. (41.3 × 27 cm.).
Signed lower center "Preston Dickinson."

52 *Outskirts of the City.* n.d.
Water color, 9⅞ × 14⅞ in. (24 × 37.8 cm.).
Signed lower left "Preston Dickinson."

53 *Grain Elevators.* 1924. *
Pastel, 24¾ × 17 15/16 in. (62.8 × 45.5 cm.).
Signed and dated lower left "Dickinson '24."

When using pastels, Dickinson fully expressed his propensity for oriental delicacy of line and tone. Here, great height is suggested by repeated, unbroken vertical strokes. Doors and windows, the only admissions of man's presence in these seemingly impenetrable towers, are reduced to tiny, decorative elements. The massive and ungainly grain elevators appear highly fragile without becoming totally divorced from their original function.

EXHIBITIONS: Arts Club of Chicago, 1939; John Herron Art Institute, Indianapolis, Indiana, "Water Colors by American Artists," 1 February–8 March 1944; Indiana University Museum of Art, Bloomington, Indiana, 10–25 March 1944; American Federation of Arts, New York, "Early Twentieth Century American Water Colors," circulating exhibition, 1 August 1948–1 June 1949; Carnegie Institute, 1952; Museum of Fine Arts, St. Petersburg, 1968.

54 *Still Life, No. 1.* c. 1924. *
Oil on canvas, 24 × 20 in. (61 × 50.8 cm.).
Signed upper right "P. Dickinson."

The subtle, carefully balanced color in this elegant still life is characteristic of Dickinson's later oils. His earlier tendency to clutter such works with an excessive number of bright color areas has now been controlled.

Still Life No. 1 is tightly composed but less terse than Dickinson's water color landscapes; his arbitrary use of light and shade for accent lends informality to the composition.

EXHIBITIONS: Daniel Gallery, New York, "Recent Pastels by Preston Dickinson," 10 February–5 March 1927, no. 2; Museum of Living Art, New York University, New York, "Opening Exhibition," 13 December 1927–25 January 1928; Art Institute of Chicago, Chicago, Illinois, "Century of Progress Exhibition of Paintings and Sculpture," 1 June–1 November 1934, no. 572; Cincinnati Art Museum, 1935; Museum of Fine Arts, St. Petersburg, 1968.
REPRODUCED: *New York Times Magazine*, 20 July 1924; *Arts*, vol. 8, August 1925, p. 90.

55 *Still Life, No. 2.* n.d. *
Oil on canvas, 20 × 18 in. (51 × 45.7 cm.).
Signed lower right "P. Dickinson."

EXHIBITIONS: Carnegie Institute, 1952; Allentown Art Museum, Allentown, Pennsylvania, 1–18 April 1961.

56 *Still Life, No. 3.* 1924.
Pastel, 14 × 16¾ in. (35.5 × 42.5 cm.).
Signed lower left "Dickinson."

57 *Hospitality*. c. 1926. *
Pastel, 21¼ × 13½ in. (54 × 34.2 cm.).
Signed lower right "Preston Dickinson."

Dickinson's still lifes were, for the most part, substantial and volumetric. In *Hospitality*, however, planes and volumes are rendered with a precision more typical of his landscape or figure studies. As the title indicates, the artist has abandoned purely formal relationships in favor of a very personal attitude toward this classic subject.

EXHIBITIONS: Knoedler Galleries, New York, "Preston Dickinson Exhibition of Paintings," February 1943, no. 24; John Herron Art Institute, Indianapolis, Indiana, "Water Colors by American Artists," 1 February–8 March 1944; Indiana University Museum of Art, Bloomington, Indiana, 10–25 March 1944; American Federation of Arts, New York, "Early Twentieth Century American Water Colors," circulating exhibition, 1 August 1948–1 June 1949.

REPRODUCED: Born, Wolfgang. *Still-Life Painting in America*. New York, 1947, pl. 128.

58 *Still Life with Yellow Green Chair*. 1928. *
Oil on canvas, 15 × 21 in. (38.2 × 53.3 cm.).
Signed lower center "Dickinson."

EXHIBITIONS: Museum of Living Art, New York University, New York, "Opening Exhibition," 13 December 1927–25 January 1928; Museum of Modern Art, New York, "Paintings by Nineteen Living Americans," 13 December 1929–12 January 1930, no. 17, illus. p. 23; Museum of Modern Art, New York, "Art in Progress," 24 May–15 October 1944, illus. p. 78; Carnegie Institute, 1952; Contemporary Arts Center of Cincinnati Art Museum and Dayton Art Institute, Ohio, "An American Viewpoint: Realism in the Twentieth Century," 10 October 1957–15 January 1958, illus.; Walker Art Center, 1960, illus. after p. 45; Indiana University Museum of Art, Bloomington, Indiana, "American Painting 1910 to 1960," 19 April–10 May 1964, no. 20, illus.; Smithsonian Institution, Washington, D.C., "Roots of Abstract Art in America 1910–1930," 1 December 1965–16 January 1966, no. 41; University of New Mexico Art Museum, 1967, illus. p. 28; American Federation of Arts, New York, "American Still-Life Painting 1913–1917," circulating exhibition, October 1967–October 1968.

REPRODUCED: *Art News*, 14 December 1929, p. 7; *The Arts*, vol. 16, January 1930, p. 30; Kootz, Samuel. *Modern American Painters*, New York, 1930, pl. 15; *Creative Art*, vol. 8, May 1931, p. 337; McMahon, Philip. "New Books on Art," *Parnassus* (College Art Association New York), December 1936; Brown, Milton. *American Painting from the Armory Show to the Depression*. Princeton, 1955, p. 129.

Arthur G. Dove (1880–1946)

Born Canandaigua, New York, 1880. Began painting in early childhood. Attended Hobart College, Geneva, New York, for two years, and Cornell University, Ithaca, for two years where he took art courses under Charles Wellington Furlong. Went to New York City after graduating from Cornell in 1903 and became, from 1904 to 1908, a successful illustrator for *Harper's Magazine*, *Collier's*, *Saturday Evening Post*, *McClure's* and others. Married first wife, 1904. Continued painting in spare time. Went to France and Italy in 1908 for eighteen months. In Paris he became friends with Alfred Maurer, met Arthur Carles and Jo Davidson. Exhibited in Paris Salon d'Automne, 1908 and 1909. Stayed in Cagnes until return to U.S. in 1910. Invited by Stieglitz to join "291" group that year; remained a friend of Stieglitz until his death. Began painting highly abstract works about 1910. Works shown in "Younger American Painters Show" at Stieglitz' Gallery of the Photo-Secession in 1910 and in "Forum Exhibition" organized by Stieglitz in 1912. First one-man show at Stieglitz' gallery in 1912; show was sent to W. Scott Thurber Galleries, Chicago. Purchased farm in Westport, Connecticut, in 1910 where attempted to support self and family until about 1918. Exhibited at the National Arts Club, 1914, at the second "Forum Exhibition" at Anderson Galleries, 1916, and at the New York Society of Independent Artists' annual exhibition, 1917. Around 1920, left first wife to live in a yawl on Long Island Sound where he began to produce collages. Married second wife, the painter Helen Torr, during this period. Exhibited at the Pennsylvania Academy of Fine Arts in 1921, Anderson Galleries in 1922 and 1924 and Stieglitz' new Intimate Gallery in 1925. The collector Duncan Phillips, Dove's sole patron for many years, bought his first Dove from one-man show at the Intimate Gallery in 1926. Works also shown in *Société Anonyme*'s "International Exhibition of Modern Art," 1927. Dove moved to Ketewomeke Yacht Club, Halesite, Long Island, around 1929. Began annual exhibitions at An American Place Gallery in 1929, continued to 1946. Works in Museum of Modern Art show, 1931, Whitney Museum 1932–1933. Sold boat and returned to parents' home in Geneva when widowed mother died in 1934. Remained there until 1938. Developed Bright's Disease and a chronic heart condition. Around 1938 he moved with his wife to unused roller rink in Geneva, then returned to Long Island that year and bought abandoned post office in Centerport where he lived until his death in 1946.

BIBLIOGRAPHY: McCausland, E. "Dove, Man and Painter," *Parnassus*, IX, December 1937, pp. 3–6; Baldinger, Wallace Spencer. "Formal Change in Recent American Painting," *Art Bulletin*, XIX, December 1937, pp. 580–591; Phillips, Duncan. "Arthur G. Dove, 1880–1946," *Magazine of Art*, XL, May 1947, pp. 193–197; Goldwater, Robert. "Arthur Dove, A Pioneer of Abstract Expressionism in American Art," *Perspectives U.S.A.* (New York), no. 2, Winter 1953, pp. 78–88; "Arthur G. Dove 1880–1946: A Retrospective Exhibition," catalogue, Andrew Dickinson White Museum of Art, Cornell University, November 1954, introduction by Alan R. Solomon; "Arthur G. Dove," cata-

54 Preston Dickinson *Still Life No.* 1 c. 1924

57 Preston Dickinson *Hospitality* c. 1926

59 Arthur G. Dove *Movement No.* 1 c. 1911

logue, University of California, Berkeley, 1958, introduction by Frederick S. Wight, see p. 35 and p. 46 for references to paintings in the Howald Collection; Ray, Martin W. "Arthur G. Dove, the Boldest Pioneer," *Arts*, vol. XXXII, September 1958, pp. 34–41; Kramer, Hilton. "The Loneliness of Arthur Dove," *New York Times*, 19 March 1963, p. D-27; "Arthur Dove: the Years of Collage," catalogue, University of Maryland Art Gallery, 13 March–19 April 1967, introduction by Dorothy Rylander Johnson.

59 *Movement No. 1*. c. 1911. *
Pastel on canvas mounted on pasteboard, $21\frac{3}{8} \times 18$ in. (54.3 × 45.7 cm.).

Arthur Dove was an isolated and avant-garde figure in the history of twentieth-century painting. He was perhaps the first painter to produce totally abstract works, antedating Kandinsky's abstractions of 1911 by about a year.

Interested in depicting sensations rather than facts, he tried to paint what was for him the "reality" of nature—a reality of forces, colors, and masses rather than of specific objects. *Movement No. 1* was later entitled *Nature Symbolized*; it was shown by Stieglitz in 1912 with other undated works of the same name. Here, forms are concentrated and simplified by means of movement toward and away from a single focal point.

EXHIBITIONS: Cincinnati Art Museum, Cincinnati, Ohio, "Paintings: 1900–1925," 2 February–4 March 1951, no. 49; Carnegie Institute, 1952; Art Galleries of University of California, Los Angeles, "Arthur G. Dove Retrospective Exhibition," circulating exhibition to Whitney Museum, New York, Phillips Gallery, Washington, D.C., Museum of Fine Arts, Boston, Marion Koogler McNay Art Institute, San Antonio, Art Center at La Jolla, California, San Francisco Museum of Art, October 1958–September 1959, no. 5; Corcoran Gallery, Washington, D.C., "The New Tradition," 27 April–2 June 1963, no. 34, illus. p. 24; Public Education Association, New York, "Seven Decades of Modern Art, 1895–1965," 26 April–21 May 1966, no. 100, illus. p. 62.

60 *Thunderstorm*. 1921. *
Oil, with silver and gold-bronze paint, on canvas, $21\frac{1}{2} \times 18\frac{1}{8}$ in. (54.5 × 46 cm.)
Signed and dated on back "Dove 1921."

This painting is more explicit and yet more mystical than Dove's earlier renditions of the same theme. By concentrating on painterly elements, he communicates the intensity of his feelings toward nature, capturing the essence rather than the appearance of natural phenomena. The jagged, schematic treatment of lightning and storm clouds is suggestive of American Indian art, relating abstraction to a native rather than European tradition. By focusing on a personal, non-objective approach to the subject, Dove reveals himself. "Everything we do," he said, "is a self-portrait."

EXHIBITIONS: Cincinnati Art Museum, 1935; Taft Museum, Cincinnati, Ohio, "The Cincinnati Biennial Festival of the Arts," 27 January–18 March 1951; Carnegie Institute, 1952; Norfolk Museum, Norfolk, Virginia, "Significant American Moderns," March–April 1953; Art Galleries of University of California, Los Angeles, "Arthur G. Dove Retrospective Exhibition," circulating exhibition (see entry 58), October 1958–September 1959, no. 13.

REPRODUCED: Stites, Raymond. *The Arts and Man*. New York, 1940, p. 812; *see* Baldinger, W. S. "Formal Change in Recent American Painting," *Art Bulletin*, vol. XIX, December 1937, p. 586.

Elsie Driggs (1898–1955)

61 *Cineraria*. n.d.
Pastel, $16\frac{5}{8} \times 13\frac{5}{16}$ in. (42.3 × 33.8 cm.).
Signed lower right "Elsie Driggs."

William Glackens (1870–1938)

Born in Philadelphia, 1870. Graduated from Central High School. Became reporter-illustrator for the *Philadelphia Record* in 1891. Switched to the *Philadelphia Press* in 1892 where George Luks, John Sloan and Everett Shinn also worked. Remained with the *Press*, except for a brief association with the *Ledger*, until 1895. Studied part time during this period at Pennsylvania Academy of Fine Arts. Exhibited at the Academy's annual show in 1894. Travelled to Europe in 1895, first to Belgium and Holland, then to France where he rented a studio in Paris. Exhibited in the Paris Salon, 1895. Returned to U.S. in 1896 to New York City. Did comic drawings for the *New York World* and illustrations for the *New York Herald*, *McClure's*, *Scribner's* and the *Saturday Evening Post*. Sent to Cuba in 1898 by *McClure's* to cover the Spanish-American War; this was his last full time job as a reporter-illustrator. Exhibited in Paris Exposition, 1900. Visited Newfoundland, 1902. Worked on commission for *Scribner's* from 1899 to 1902. Illustrated English-language edition of works of Charles Paul de Kock, 1904. Married Edith Demock, an art student, in 1904. Exhibited at National Arts Club, New York 1904. Second trip to Europe in 1906; went to Madrid to study Velasquez' works in the Prado, then to Paris where he painted for several months. Works appeared with those of *The Eight* at Macbeth Gallery, New York, 1908. Helped organize first Independent's exhibition, New York, 1910, in which his own work was included. Went to Paris in 1912 to purchase art for Dr. Albert C. Barnes, a high school classmate. Trip brought Glackens in intimate contact with contemporary French painting. Stayed with Alfred Maurer in Paris. Returned to U.S. with works by Manet, Renoir, Cézanne, Van Gogh and others that became nucleus of Barnes' collection. Helped organize Armory Show in 1913; was chairman of committee for selection of American section. First president of Society of Independent Artists, 1916 and 1917. Returned to France in 1925; next seven years spent in Paris and New York. Remained in U.S. after 1932. Elected to National Academy, 1933. Awarded Grand Prix, Paris Exhibition, 1937. Died 1938.

BIBLIOGRAPHY: Watson, Forbes. "William Glackens," *Arts*, vol. III, no. 4, April 1923, pp. 246–261; DuBois, Guy Pène. *William J. Glackens*. American Artists Group, New York, 1931; Glackens, Ira. *William Glackens and the Ashcan Group: the Emergence of Realism in American Art*. New York, 1957; *Quarterly Journal of Current Acquisitions*, Library of Congress, vol. 20, no. 1, December 1962, discussion of Glackens' Spanish-American war drawings in Library collection, pp. 12–18; "The Art of William Glackens," catalogue, Rutgers University, 10 January–10 February 1967 (*University Art Gallery Bulletin*, vol. 1, no. 1), introduction by Richard J. Wattenmaker.

62 *Pier at Blue Point*. 1914. *
Oil on canvas, 25⅞ × 32 in. (65.7 × 81.3 cm.).
Signed lower left "W. Glackens."

EXHIBITIONS: Cincinnati Art Museum, 1935; City Art Museum of St. Louis, "William Glackens in Retrospect," 18 November–31 December 1966, circulating exhibition to Smithsonian Institution, Washington, D.C., 9 February–2 April 1967, Whitney Museum, 25 April–11 June 1967, no. 42, illus.; Museum of Fine Arts, St. Petersburg, 1968.

63 *Beach Scene, New London*. 1918. *
Oil on canvas, 26 × 31⅞ in. (66 × 81 cm.).
Signed lower left "W. Glackens."

Glackens, associated with *The Eight* from the time of the group's first exhibition in 1908, painted commonplace subjects, scandalizing his public and giving him an unwanted notoriety. Although the theme no longer seems remarkable, this painting remains outstanding by virtue of its fresh color and lively, flexible composition.

Glackens drew his inspiration for such works largely from Renoir, but was never a mere imitator of the European master. Like many artists of his time, he visited Europe frequently, but returned home to adapt a continental style into a personal, native idiom. Here, the robust color and dry, rapid brushwork serve as a perfect vehicle for the enthusiasm and gaiety of an American beach scene.

EXHIBITIONS: Whitney Museum, New York, "William J. Glackens Memorial Exhibition," 14 December 1938–15 January 1939, no. 42; Carnegie Institute, Pittsburgh, Pennsylvania, "Memorial Exhibition of Works by William J. Glackens," 1 February–15 March 1939, no. 12; Carnegie Institute, 1952; Marquette University, Milwaukee, Wisconsin, "Festival of American Arts," 20 April–20 May 1956; Contemporary Arts Center of Cincinnati Art Museum and Dayton Art Institute, Ohio, "An American Viewpoint: Realism in the Twentieth Century," 10 October 1957–15 January 1958; American Federation of Arts, New York, "American Impressionists, Two Generations," October 1963–May 1965, no. 11; City Art Museum of St. Louis, "William Glackens in Retrospect," 18 November–31 December 1966, circulating exhibition (see entry 62), no. 54; Museum of Fine Arts, St. Petersburg, 1968.

REPRODUCED: *The Arts*, vol. 8, August 1925, p. 74; Glackens, Ira. *William Glackens and the Ashcan Group; the Emergence of Realism in American Art*. New York, 1957, after p. 236.

64 *Bathing Near the Bay*. 1919. *
Oil on canvas, 18 × 23⅞ in. (45.8 × 60.6 cm.).
Signed lower right "W. Glackens."

Even in his most impressionistic landscapes, Glackens retains the quality of direct observation he acquired in his years of work as a newspaper artist. A specific time and locale are implied despite Glackens' subordination of naturalistic detail, as in this work where the mellow and hazy tonalities of sky and water predominate.

EXHIBITIONS: University of New Mexico, Albuquerque, New Mexico, "Impressionism in America," February–March 1965, circulating exhibition to M. H. De Young Memorial Museum, San Francisco, March–May 1965, no. 19; Grand Rapids Art Museum, Grand Rapids, Michigan, "Twentieth Century American Paintings," 1–30 April 1967; Museum of Fine Arts, St. Petersburg, 1968.

Marsden Hartley (1877–1943)

Born Lewiston, Maine, 1877. Made drawings for local naturalist at age 13. Received scholarship to Cleveland School of Art in 1892. Studied at Chase School, New York, with William Merritt Chase, Frank Vincent DuMond and F. Luis Mora from 1898 to 1899. Attended National Academy of Design in 1900. Lived and painted during summer in Maine, during winter in New York from 1901 to 1908. Frequently worked in Maine during the summer for the rest of his life. First one-man show at Gallery of the Photo-Secession, 1909, where his works also appeared in "Younger American Painters" shown in 1910. Second one-man show at Gallery of the

60 Arthur G. Dove *Thunderstorm* 1921

William Glackens *Pier at Blue Point* 1914

63 William Glackens *Beach Scene, New London* 1918

64 William Glackens *Bathing Near the Bay* 1919

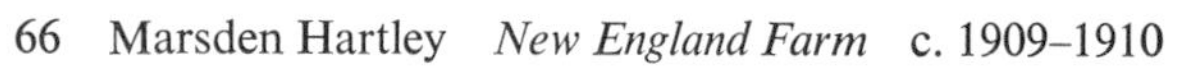

66 Marsden Hartley *New England Farm* c. 1909–1910

67 Marsden Hartley *The Mountain, Autumn* 1910–1911

69 Marsden Hartley *Still Life No.* 1 1913

71 Marsden Hartley *Composition* 1914

68 Marsden Hartley *Desertion* 1912

72 Marsden Hartley *Berlin Ante-War* c. 1914–1915

Photo-Secession, 1912. Went to Paris in 1912, with financial assistance from Stieglitz and Arthur B. Davies, where he saw works of Courbet for first time. Travelled regularly between Europe and U.S. from 1912 to 1916. Exhibited in Armory Show, 1913, and in Autumn Salon organized in Germany by Der Sturm. Works shown at Daniel Gallery, New York, 1915, and at the home of Max Liebermann in Berlin; showed with Der Blaue Reiter, 1915 to 1916, at invitation of Franz Marc. Works appeared in "Forum Exhibition," Anderson Galleries, 1916. Visited Bermuda in 1916. Went to Taos and Santa Fe, New Mexico, to paint in 1918. Returned to New York in 1919. Exhibition at Montross Gallery, New York, and paintings in Société Anonyme's fifth exhibition in 1920. Highly successful auction of paintings in 1921 at Anderson Galleries allowed Hartley to return to Europe on proceeds of sale. In Berlin, 1922 to 1923. Also visited Vienna, Florence and Rome. First book of poetry published in Paris, 1922. Lived part of 1924 and most of 1925 in Vence, France. Lived in New York, Aix-en-Provence and Paris in 1927. Exhibition at Arts Club, Chicago, 1928. Returned to New York in 1930. Works shown at the Intimate Gallery, An American Place and the Downtown Gallery, New York, in 1920's and 1930's. Travelled to Mexico in 1932 on Guggenheim Fellowship awarded to him the previous year. Visited Nova Scotia in 1935 and 1936. Died in Ellsworth, Maine, 1943.

BIBLIOGRAPHY: Hartley, Marsden. *Adventures in the Arts*. New York, 1921; Hartley, Marsden. "Art and the Personal Life," *Creative Art*, vol. II, June 1928, pp. xxxi–xxxiv; Phillips, Duncan. "Marsden Hartley," *Magazine of Art*, vol. 37, no. 3, March 1944, pp. 83–87; "Lyonel Feininger and Marsden Hartley," catalogue, Museum of Modern Art, New York, October 1944–January 1945, forward by Monroe Wheeler; Wells, Henry W. "The Pictures and Poems of Marsden Hartley," *Magazine of Art*, vol. XXXVIII, January 1945, pp. 26–32; Hartley, Marsden. *Selected Poems*. New York, 1945; Gallup, Donald. "The Weaving of a Pattern: Marsden Hartley and Gertrude Stein," *Magazine of Art*, Vol. XLI, November 1948, pp. 256–261; McCausland, Elizabeth. "Return of the Native: Marsden Hartley," *Art in America*, vol. XL, no. 2, 1952, pp. 55–79; McCausland, Elizabeth. *Marsden Hartley*. Minneapolis, 1952; Mellquist, Jerome. "Marsden Hartley," *Perspectives U.S.A.*, no. 4, 1953, pp. 62–77; Munson, Graham. "The Painter from Maine," *Arts*, vol. XXXV, February 1961, pp. 32–41; Kramer, Hilton. "Hartley and Modern Painting," *Arts*, vol. XXXV, February 1961, pp. 42–45; Alloway, Lawrence. "Berlin or Maine," *The Arts Review*, vol. 13, no. 12, 1–5 July 1961, p. 11; Davidson, A. "Cubism and the Early American Modernist," *Art Journal*, vol. 26, no. 2, winter 1966–67, pp. 122–129.

65 *The Mountains*. 1909. *
Oil on canvas, 30 × 30⅛ in. (76.1 × 76.5 cm.).
Signed lower right "Marsden Hartley."

Around 1908, when Hartley lived in New York and summered in Maine, he became fascinated by the style of the Italian-born painter Segantini, whose heavily impastoed, stitch-like brushstroke was adapted by him in this early version of *The Mountains*. Flecks of vivid color are used here to capture the strength and intricacy of the Maine countryside Hartley loved.

He constantly returned to the same subject, feeling that each version of the mountain brought him closer to capturing nature's "truth."

EXHIBITIONS: Cincinnati Art Museum, Cincinnati, Ohio, "Marsden Hartley—Stuart Davis," 24 October–24 November 1941.

66 *New England Farm*. c. 1909–1910. *
Oil on wood panel, 12¼ × 12¼ in. (35 × 35 cm.).
Signed lower right "Marsden Hartley."

EXHIBITIONS: Museum of Modern Art, New York, "Lyonel Feininger and Marsden Hartley," 24 October 1944–14 January 1945; Taft Museum, Cincinnati, Ohio, "The Cincinnati Biennial Festival of the Arts," 27 January–18 March 1951; Norfolk Museum, Norfolk, Virginia, "Significant American Moderns," March–April 1953; Museum of Fine Arts, St. Petersburg, 1968.

67 *The Mountain, Autumn*. 1910–1911. *
Oil on wood panel, 12¼ × 12¼ in. (35 × 35 cm.).
Signed lower right "Marsden Hartley."

EXHIBITIONS: Taft Museum, Cincinnati, Ohio, "The Cincinnati Biennial Festival of the Arts," 27 January–18 March 1951; Norfolk Museum, Norfolk, Virginia, "Significant American Moderns," March–April 1953; Museum of Fine Arts, St. Petersburg, 1968.

68 *Desertion*. 1912. *
Oil on wood panel, 14 × 22 in. (35.7 × 55.7 cm.).

69 *Still Life No. 1*. 1913.
Oil on canvas, 31½ × 25⅝ in. (80 × 65 cm.).
Signed lower left "Marsden Hartley."

EXHIBITIONS: Cincinnati Art Museum, Cincinnati, Ohio, "Pictures for Peace; A Retrospective from the Armory Show of 1913," 18 March–16 April 1944, no. 12; Cincinnati Art Museum, Cincinnati, Ohio, "Paintings: 1900–1925," 2 February–4 March 1951, no. 51, illus.; Amherst College, Amherst, Massachusetts, "The 1913 Armory Show in Retrospect," 17 February–30 March 1958; Ohio Wesleyan University, Delaware, Ohio, 13 November–13 December 1959; Munson-Williams-Proctor Institute, Utica, New York, "Armory Show, Fiftieth Anniversary," 17 February–28 April 1963; Museum of Fine Arts, St. Petersburg, 1968.

70 *Still Life No. 2*. 1913.
Oil on wood panel, 9¼ × 13 in. (23.5 × 33 cm.).

71 *Composition*. 1914. *
Oil on canvas, 39½ × 31⅛ in. (100.2 × 81 cm.).

EXHIBITIONS: Norfolk Museum, Norfolk, Virginia, "Significant American Moderns," March–April 1953.

72 *Berlin Ante-War*. c. 1914–1915. *
Oil on canvas, 39¼ × 31⅞ in. (100 × 81 cm.).

In July, 1914, Hartley left for a second trip to Europe. By 1915, he was in Berlin, painting what he termed "prewar pageants." Hartley considered these purely pictorial rather than symbolic pictures, although their emblematic style has certain symbolic overtones. With their bright, clear tones and softened brushwork, they are reminiscent of the Coptic embroideries whose texture and color the artist admired.

By compartmentalizing images within a repeated series of geometric shapes, a hieratic and ordered framework is created to express the ritualistic gaiety of pre-war Germany. Bright, bold and deceptively simple, these works prefigure the "Pop" paintings of the 1960's, especially those of Robert Indiana.

EXHIBITIONS: Cincinnati Art Museum, Cincinnati, Ohio, "Marsden Hartley—Stuart Davis," 24 October–24 November 1941; Museum of Fine Arts, St. Petersburg, 1968.

73 *Still Life with Grapes*. c. 1915.
Oil on canvas, 23¼ × 43 in. (59 × 109 cm.).

74 *Bowl with Fruit*. 1919.
Oil on canvas, 13¾ × 25¾ in. (35 × 65.3 cm.).
Penciled on stretcher "Bowl with Fruit Marsden Hartley."

75 *Fruit*. 1919.
Pastel, 7¾ × 8⅜ in. (19.5 × 21 cm.).
Signed lower right "M. Hartley."

76 *Sail Boat*. c. 1919. *
Oil on pasteboard, 16 × 12⅛ in. (40.5 × 30.7 cm.).
Signed lower left "Marsden Hartley."

Hartley's reaction to the Dada revolution, which began in 1916 in Zurich and had a profound effect on many American painters of the decade, is expressed in his use of mundane objects; these objects are rendered not in social realist terms, but serve as a "delectable diversion." The Dada idea that all things have equal significance appealed to Hartley as a means of achieving new freedom in his work. Although he believed that art was above all a product of intelligence, Dadaism allowed him to incorporate humorous spontaneity into an otherwise rational approach. *Sailboat*, in its simplification and whimsical ordering of shapes, reflects this new influence.

EXHIBITIONS: Hackley Art Gallery, Muskegon, Michigan, "Old Masters of Modern Art," 6 October–17 November 1958.

77 *Lilies in a Vase*. c. 1920.
Oil on heavy pasteboard, 27 × 19⅛ in. (68.5 × 48.5 cm.).

78 *Color Analogy*. c. 1921. *
Oil on wood panel, 20 × 15⅝ in. (50.7 × 40 cm.).

In 1921 Hartley returned to Europe, where he began a series of abstract, cubist-oriented still lifes in which objects are used as foils for a personal and expressive exploration of color problems.

Gertrude Stein, in a 1913 letter to Stieglitz, spoke of Hartley's remarkable use of color as a tangible substance. "He deals with his color," she wrote, "as actually as Picasso deals with his forms." (Museum of Modern Art, N.Y., Hartley—Feininger catalogue, 1944.)

EXHIBITIONS: University of New Mexico Art Museum, 1967, illus. p. 34; American Federation of Arts, New York, "American Still Life Painting 1913–1917," circulating exhibition, October 1967–October 1968.

79 *New Mexico Recollections*. 1923.*
Oil on canvas, 17¾ × 30⅞ in. (45.2 × 78.4 cm.).
Signed and dated on back of stretcher "1923 Marsden Hartley."

In the tradition of Ryder, Hartley's attitude toward landscape painting always remained highly romantic. In 1918 a grant from Charles Daniel enabled him to live in New Mexico, whose stark, vital landscape he loved.

Despite an earlier insistence on intellectual clarity (i.e., "correct" color relationships, an ordered and precise arrangement of forms), he began to turn, in the '20's, toward expressionism. He felt, he later stated, an increasing need to escape from "hyper-intellectualism," to return to nature itself as an artistic source. In painting his recollections of New Mexico in 1922–23, his vision became increasingly expressive and intense.

EXHIBITIONS: Cincinnati Art Museum, 1935; Museum of Fine Arts, St. Petersburg, 1968.

65 Marsden Hartley *The Mountains* 1909

76 Marsden Hartley *Sail Boat* c. 1919

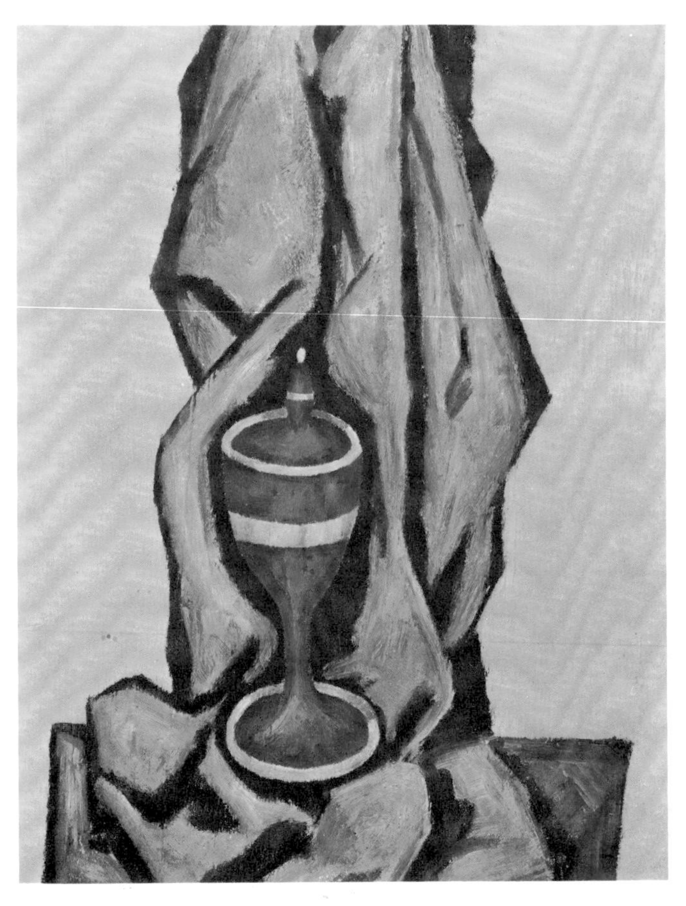

78 Marsden Hartley *Color Analogy* c. 1921

79 Marsden Hartley *New Mexico Recollections* 1923

81 Rockwell Kent *Pollock Seining* 1907

82 Rockwell Kent *Men and Mountains* 1909

85 Rockwell Kent *Pastoral* 1914

86 Rockwell Kent
Newfoundland Ice 1915

80 *The Window.* 1928.
Oil on canvas, 35⅝ × 25⅝ in. (90.4 × 65 cm.).

Rockwell Kent (1882–)

Born Tarrytown Heights, New York, 1882. Attended Columbia University, where he studied art and architecture, and William Merritt Chase's school in Shinnecock, New York. In 1900, went to the New York School on scholarship where he attended night classes taught by Robert Henri. Made first trip to Monhegan, Maine, to paint and work as a carpenter, 1906. Painted series of Monhegan marines and landscapes in 1907. Returned to New Hampshire in 1909. Sailed to Newfoundland in 1913, where he lived and painted until 1915. His first published illustrations appeared in 1914. Trip to Alaska in 1918 was financed by Ferdinand Howald. Did illustrations for *Vanity Fair* and *Harper's Monthly* under pseudonym "Hogarth, Jr." When the series of Alaska drawings appeared in 1920, Kent's work became popular. He subsequently illustrated *Candide, Moby Dick, Beowulf, The Canterbury Tales* and *Leaves of Grass*. First one-man show, Macbeth Gallery, New York, 1934. He has owned and operated a farm in the Adirondacks since 1946.

BIBLIOGRAPHY: Armitage, Merle. *Rockwell Kent.* New York, 1932; Kent, Rockwell and Carl Zigrosser. *Rockwell Kentiana.* New York, 1933; *Rockwell Kent.* American Artists Group, New York, 1945; "Robert Henri and Five of His Pupils," catalogue, The Century Association, New York, 5 April–1 June 1946.

81 *Pollock Seining.* 1907. *
Oil on canvas, 34⅛ × 43⅞ in. (82.5 × 111.5 cm.).
Signed and dated lower left "Rockwell Kent 1907."

EXHIBITIONS: Colby College, Waterville, Maine, "Maine: One Hundred Artists of the Twentieth Century," 25 June–30 September 1964, circulated by American Federation of Arts, December 1964–December 1966, note on p. 34.

82 *Men and Mountains.* 1909. *
Oil on canvas, 34⅛ × 44⅛ in. (82.5 × 112 cm.).
Signed and dated lower left "Rockwell Kent 1909."

83 *Decoration on Glass No. 1.* 1914.
Oil on glass, 9⅝ × 7⅜ in. (24.4 × 18.7 cm.).

84 *Decoration on Glass No. 2.* 1914.
Oil on glass, 7½ × 9⅝ in. (19 × 24.4 cm.).

85 *Pastoral.* 1914. *
Oil on canvas, 33⅛ × 44⅛ in. (82.5 × 112 cm.).
Signed and dated lower right "Rockwell Kent 1914."

Rockwell Kent, a student of Henri, achieved a fresh, native landscape style reminiscent of Homer and Eakins. Later, during the second decade of the century, he evolved the simple, monumental figure style typical of his well-known woodcut illustrations for *Moby Dick*, Whitman's *Leaves of Grass*, and *Candide*.

Pastoral combines his propensity for pure landscape with a mystical romanticism. The composition consists of bulky, implacably rounded shapes, suggestive of the silence and solitude Kent found in Newfoundland, where he lived at the time the work was executed.

EXHIBITIONS: Cincinnati Art Museum, 1935; Dayton Art Institute, 1941.

REPRODUCED: *Rockwell Kent.* American Artists Group, New York, 1945.

86 *Newfoundland Ice.* 1915. *
Oil on wood panel, 11⅞ × 16 in. (30.2 × 40.5 cm.).
Signed and dated lower right "Rockwell Kent 1915."

EXHIBITIONS: Dayton Art Institute, 1941; Carnegie Institute, 1952.

Yasuo Kuniyoshi (1893–1953)

Born Okayama, Japan, 1893. Came to U.S. 1906. Studied at Los Angeles School of Art for three years before 1910 when he moved to New York. Studied at Robert Henri's School, 1910; at the National Academy of Design, 1912 to 1914; at the Independent School of Art, 1914 to 1916, under Homer Boss; and the Art Students League, 1916 to 1920, under Kenneth Hayes Miller. Supported himself as student by photographing works of painters and illustrators. Works first exhibited at Society of Independent Artists and at Penguin Club in 1917. First one-man show at Daniel Gallery, 1922; showed annually there until 1930. Works exhibited at Downtown Gallery after 1930. Became interested in lithography in 1925. Travelled to Europe in 1925 and 1928. Went to Japan in 1931 for large retrospective of his work in Tokyo and Osaka. Taught at Art Students League, 1933 to 1953, at New School for Social Research, 1936 to 1953, and at Woodstock Summer Art School. Was president of Artists Equity Association from 1947 to 1950. Died New York City, 1953.

BIBLIOGRAPHY: Brook, A. "Yasuo Kuniyoshi," *Arts*, January 1924, pp. 24–27; Brace, E. "Yasuo Kuniyoshi," *Creative Art*, vol. XI, November 1932, pp. 184–188; Wheeler, Monroe. *Painters and Sculptors of Modern America.* New York, 1942, pp. 73–79; *Yasuo Kuniyoshi.* American Artists Group, New York, 1945; Goodrich, Lloyd. *Yasuo Kuniyoshi.* New York, 1948, includes catalogue of exhibition at Whitney Museum, 27 March–9 May 1948; Goodrich, Lloyd. "In Memory of Yasuo Kuniyoshi," *Art Students League News*, Special Supplement, Summer 1953; "Kokuritsu Kindai

Bijutsukan," catalogue, National Museum of Modern Art, Tokyo, 20 March–25 April 1954, text (in English and Japanese) by Atsue Imaizumi and Lloyd Goodrich; "The Graphic Works of Yasuo Kuniyoshi 1893–1953," *Journal of the Archives of American Art*, vol. 5, no. 3, July 1965, pp. 1–19.

87 *Boy Stealing Fruit*. 1923. *
Oil on canvas, 20 × 30 in. (50.7 × 76.2 cm.).
Signed and dated lower right "Yasuo Kuniyoshi '23."

EXHIBITIONS: Daniel Gallery, New York, "Kuniyoshi Retrospective Exhibition," February–March 1928, no. 2; Museum of Modern Art, New York, "Paintings by Nineteen Living Americans," 13 December–12 January 1930, no. 52, illus. p. 48; Whitney Museum, New York, "Yasuo Kuniyoshi Retrospective Exhibition," 27 March–9 May 1948, no. 11; Cincinnati Art Museum, Cincinnati, Ohio, "An American Show," 1 October–5 November 1948, no. 59, illus.; Carnegie Institute, 1952; American Federation of Arts, "Venice Biennale," 15 June–19 October 1952; Downtown Gallery, New York, "Yasuo Kuniyoshi Exhibition," 7–27 December 1952; National Museum of Modern Art, Tokyo, Japan, "Kuniyoshi," 20 March–25 April 1954, illus. pl. 2; Downtown Gallery, New York, "The Recurrent Image," 31 January–25 February 1956, no. 6; Milwaukee Art Center, Milwaukee, Wisconsin, "Artist Looks at Children," 30 October 1959–14 February 1960; Boston University Art Gallery, Boston, Massachusetts, "Yasuo Kuniyoshi Retrospective Exhibition," 24 February–18 March 1961, no. 8, illus.; Indiana University Museum of Art, Bloomington, Indiana, "American Painting 1910–1960," 19 April–10 May 1964, no. 41.

REPRODUCED: *Parnassus*, vol. 1, December 1929, p. 16; Kootz, Samuel M. *Modern American Painters*. New York, 1930, pl. 35; Cahill, Holger and Barr, Alfred H. Jr. (eds.). *Art in America in Modern Times*. New York, 1934, p. 42; Brown, Milton W. *American Painting from the Armory Show to the Depression*. Princeton, 1955, p. 157.

88 *Cock Calling the Dawn*. 1923.
Oil on canvas, 30 × 25 in. (76.2 × 63.4 cm.).

89 *The Swimmer*. c. 1924. *
Oil on canvas, 20⅛ × 30⅛ in. (51 × 76.4 cm.).

Kuniyoshi, who came to America at the age of 13, became one of the most admired and respected artists in America during the early '20's. Although at times his work reflects specific European influences, especially that of Pascin, he evolved a personal imagery in which fantastic visions derived from naturalistic sources.

In this picture, the perspective is tilted, isolating the swimmer; she appears to be both in the water and hovering over it. The island, small and remote, remains at an ambiguous distance from her. Kuniyoshi's style is precise, so that distortions of scale seem even more fantastic, although the surreal quality is tempered here by an oriental lyricism.

EXHIBITIONS: Art Institute of Chicago, Chicago, Illinois, "A Century of Progress Exhibition of Paintings and Sculpture," 1 June–1 November 1933, no. 587; Cincinnati Art Museum, 1935; Dayton Art Institute, 1941; Downtown Gallery, New York, "Twenty One Paintings by Yasuo Kuniyoshi, 1921–1941," 5–29 May 1942, no. 4; Whitney Museum, New York, "Yasuo Kuniyoshi Retrospective Exhibition," 27 March–9 May 1948, no. 21; University of Michigan Museum of Art, Ann Arbor, Michigan, "Sport and Circus," 8–29 November 1950; Carnegie Institute, 1952; Ohio Wesleyan University, Delaware, Ohio, 13 November–13 December 1959; Corcoran Gallery, Washington, D.C. "The New Tradition," 27 April–2 June 1963, no. 56, illus. p. 34; Colby College, Waterville, Maine, "Maine, 100 Artists of the Twentieth Century," 25 June–30 September 1964, circulated by American Federation of Arts, December 1964–December 1966, p. 36.

REPRODUCED: *Time Magazine*, 12 April 1948; Spaeth, E. *American Art Museums and Galleries*. New York, 1960, p. 125; *Art in America*, vol. 51, 1963, p. 74.

Ernest Lawson (1873–1939)

Born Halifax, Nova Scotia, 1873. Moved to Kansas City in 1888. Worked as engineering draughtsman in Mexico City in 1889. Came to New York City in 1891 where he studied at the Art Students League; also studied in Cos Cob, Connecticut, with J. Alden Weir and John H. Twachtman. Went to Paris to live and paint in 1893; studied at Académie Julian. Exhibited in Salon des Artistes Français, 1894. Returned to U.S. in 1896. Accepted teaching job in Columbus, Georgia, in 1897, then moved back to New York the following year. Met William Glackens in 1904. One-man exhibition at Pennsylvania Academy of Fine Arts, Philadelphia, 1907. Works shown with *The Eight* at Macbeth Gallery in 1908. Elected associate of National Academy in 1908, and a full member in 1917. Exhibited with Canadian Art Club, Toronto, from 1911 to 1915. Joined Association of American Painters and Sculptors in 1912. Works shown in Armory Show and Canadian National Exposition, 1913. Painted in Segovia and Toledo, Spain, 1916. Went to Colorado Springs in 1926 to teach at Broadmoor Art Academy, then taught at Kansas City Art Institute in 1928. Returned to New York about 1929. In 1936 he moved to Florida, where he died in 1939.

BIBLIOGRAPHY: Phillips, Duncan. "Ernest Lawson," *Magazine of Art*, vol. 3, no. 7, May 1917, pp. 257–262; Rihani, Ameen. "Landscape Painting in America: Ernest Lawson," *International Studio*, vol. 72, no. 287, February 1921, pp. cxiv–cxvii; Price, F. N. "Lawson of the Crushed Jewels," *International Studio*, vol. LXXVIII, February 1924, pp. 367–370; DuBois, Guy Pène. *Ernest Lawson*. American

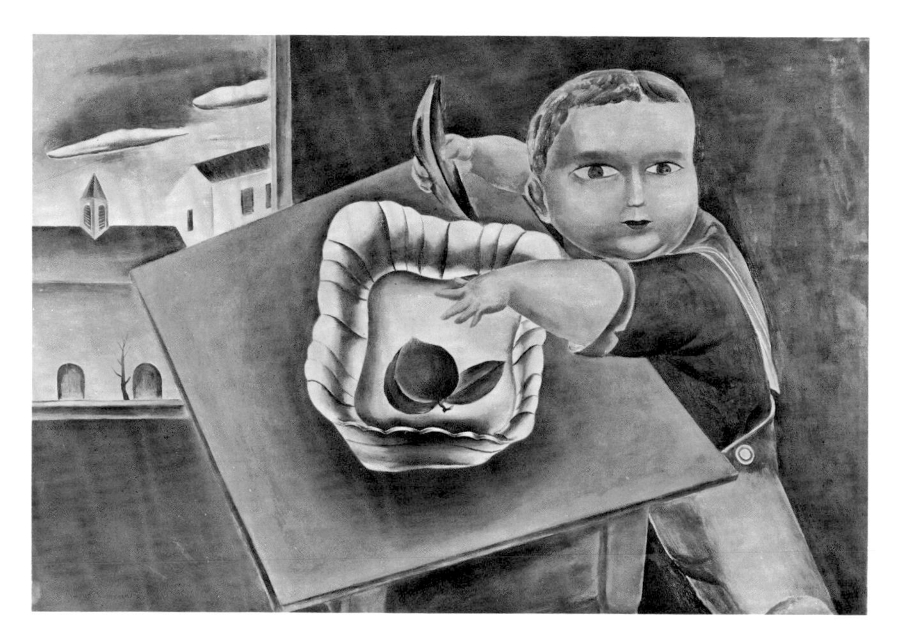

87 Yasuo Kuniyoshi *Boy Stealing Fruit* 1923

89 Yasuo Kuniyoshi *The Swimmer* c. 1924

90 Ernest Lawson *Hills at Inwood* 1914

92 Ernest Lawson *Winter Glow* n.d.

93 Ernest Lawson *Cathedral Heights* n.d.

94 Ernest Lawson *Hudson River at Inwood* n.d.

Artists Group, New York, 1932; "As Ever, Ernest," *Art Digest*, vol. xiv, 1 January 1940, p. 10, excerpts from Lawson's letters; "Noted American Impressionists—Lawson, Robinson, Hassam—Exhibited," *Art Digest*, vol. 17, no. 14, 15 April 1943, pp. 5–6; Perlman, Bennard B. *The Immortal Eight*. New York, 1962; Berry-Hill, Henry and Sidney. *Ernest Lawson, American Impressionist, 1873–1939*. Leigh-on-Sea, England, 1968, forward by Ira Glackens.

90 *Hills at Inwood*. 1914. *
Oil on canvas, 36 × 50 in. (91.4 × 127 cm.).
Signed and dated lower right "E. Lawson 1914."

Lawson was the only member of *The Eight* to paint pure landscapes. Shortly before his death, in a letter to the critic F. K. Price, he expressed his belief that color could be used to depict "the three major emotions in a man's life—anticipation, realization, and retrospection."

In *Hills at Inwood*, Lawson's fresh, sparkling color and fragmented paint surface (referred to by Price as a "palette of crushed jewels") indicate the influence of the European Impressionists. Unlike them, however, Lawson differentiated the natural features in his landscapes from each other by means of textural and chromatic variations.

EXHIBITIONS: Art Institute of Chicago, Chicago, Illinois, "Half Century of American Art," 16 November 1939–7 January 1940, no. 100; Fine Arts Gallery of San Diego, San Diego, California, "Modern American Painting 1915," 7 December 1962–6 January 1963, no. 26; National Gallery of Canada, Ottawa, "Ernest Lawson Exhibition," January 1967–January 1968, no. 31, illus. p. 28.

REPRODUCED: Berry-Hill, Henry and Sidney. *Ernest Lawson, American Impressionist 1873–1939*. England, 1968, pl. 40.

91 *The Valley*. n.d.
Oil on canvas, 20 × 24 in. (50.7 × 61 cm.).
Signed lower right "E. Lawson."

92 *Winter Glow*. n.d. *
Oil on canvas, 16 × 20⅛ in. (40.6 × 51 cm.).
Signed lower left "E. Lawson."

EXHIBITIONS: Cincinnati Art Museum, 1935; Carnegie Institute, 1952.

93 *Cathedral Heights*. n.d. *
Oil on canvas, 25⅛ × 30⅛ in. (63.8 × 76.4 cm.).
Signed lower left "E. Lawson."

EXHIBITIONS: Dayton Art Institute, Dayton, Ohio, "America and Impressionism," 19 October–11 November 1951.

REPRODUCED: Berry-Hill, Henry and Sidney. *Ernest Lawson, American Impressionist 1873–1939*. Leigh-on-Sea, England, 1968, pl. 81.

94 *Hudson River at Inwood*. n.d. *
Oil on canvas, 30 × 40 in. (76.2 × 101.5 cm.).
Signed lower right "E. Lawson."

Lawson's strength as a landscapist was due not only to his sumptuous use of color, but to the lyrical sensibility with which he rendered the Hudson River area. Thus, he afforded throughout the 1920's a continuation of the tradition established by the Hudson River School almost a century earlier; indeed Lawson considered himself a traditionalist.

His friend, Somerset Maugham, viewed him somewhat differently, using him as the basis for a moving portrayal of the tormented painter "Frederick Lawson" in *Of Human Bondage*.

EXHIBITIONS: Luxembourg Museum, Paris, "Exposition d'artistes de l'école américaine," October–November 1919; Dayton Art Institute, Dayton, Ohio, "America and Impressionism," 19 October–11 November 1951.

REPRODUCED: *The Arts*, vol. 8, August 1925, p. 73; *American Magazine of Art*, Oct., 1918, p. 185; Berry-Hill, Henry and Sidney. *Ernest Lawson, American Impressionist, 1873–1939*. Leigh-on-Sea, England, 1968, pl. 75.

95 *Birch Woods*. n.d.
Oil on canvas, 24½ × 29⅝ in. (62.2 × 75.2 cm.).
Signed lower right "E. Lawson."

96 *Early Summer—Vermont*. n.d.
Oil on canvas, 24 × 30 in. (60.9 × 76.2 cm.).
Signed lower right "E. Lawson."

George Luks (1867–1933)

Born Williamsport, Pennsylvania, 1867. Studied art in early 1880's at Pennsylvania Academy of Fine Arts in Philadelphia. Was an amateur boxer, known as 'Lusty Luks,' while a student. Left for Europe to continue studies in 1885, remaining abroad for ten years. Studied at Dusseldorf Academy and later painted and studied in Paris and in London. Influenced more by works of Rembrandt, Hals, Goya and Manet than by his formal training. Returned to U.S. around 1895. Became reporter-illustrator for the *Philadelphia Press* in 1895 where he met Sloan, Glackens and Shinn. Was Spanish-American war correspondent in Cuba for the *Evening Bulletin* in 1896. Moved to New York City in 1897. Illustrated news stories for the *New York World* and drew comics "Hogans Alley," "The Yellow Kid" and "McFadden's Flats," for the *World* and the *Journal*. Gave up journalism when his paintings became popular. The National Academy of Design rejected one of his paintings, over the objections of his friend Robert Henri, in 1907. Luks subsequently exhibited with *The Eight* at the Macbeth Gallery in 1908. His works were shown in the Armory Show in 1913. He taught at the Art Students League until a dispute arose over his colorful classroom language and he left to start his own school, the George Luks School of Painting, later directed by John Sloan. He spent the rest of his life in New York City, with brief interludes in New England, Nova Scotia and Pennsylvania. He died while sketching on a New York City street in 1933.

BIBLIOGRAPHY: De Casseres, Benjamin. "The Fantastic George Luks," *New York Herald Tribune*, 10 September 1933, p. 11; Glackens, Ira. *William Glackens and the Ashcan Group; the Emergence of Realism in American Art*. New York, 1957; Perlman, Bennard B. *The Immortal Eight*. New York, 1962.

97 *Playing Soldiers*. 1915. *
Pastel on water color, 13⅜ × 14¾ in. (34 × 37.4 cm.).
Signed lower right "George Luks."

A colorful and self-proclaimed revolutionary among *The Eight* (otherwise known as "The Ashcan School"), Luks was once referred to as "the Dickens of the East Side." He was a flamboyant chronicler of New York street life, whose gusty style and social conscience were hallmarks of the modern movement; he was, however, less concerned with formal innovations than were his European contemporaries.

Playing Soldiers, with its swift, spontaneous surface and vague figures, exemplifies the robust yet intimate sensibility of his finest paintings.

EXHIBITIONS: Newark Museum, Newark, New Jersey, "Memorial Exhibition of George Luks," 30 October 1934–6 January 1935, no. 99; Albany Institute, 1958; American Federation of Arts, New York, "Adventures in Collecting," October 1958–October 1960.

98 *Gossip*. 1915. *
Pastel on water color, 13⅜ × 14¾ in. (34 × 37.4 cm.).
Signed lower left "George Luks."

EXHIBITIONS: Newark Museum, Newark, New Jersey, "Memorial Exhibition of George Luks," 30 October 1934–6 January 1935, no. 101.

99 *The Harlem River*. 1915.
Pastel on water color, 14 × 15½ in. (35.5 × 39.3 cm.).
Signed lower right "George Luks."

Macdonald-Wright *see* Wright

Man Ray (1890–)

Born Emmanuel Radenski in Philadelphia, 1890. Moved with parents to New York City in 1897. Drew and painted as a child. Awarded university scholarship to study architecture but declined it to pursue career as painter. Studied painting in evening classes at the National Academy of Design in 1908. Attended life drawing classes at Ferrar Center, where Robert Henri and George Bellows lectured. Paintings first exhibited at Ferrar Center in 1912. Moved to artists' colony in Ridgefield, New Jersey, in 1913, where he shared a house with the painter, Sam Halpert, and met his first wife Donna Loupov, a poetess whom he married in 1914. First one-man show of paintings at the Daniel Gallery in 1915, for which he made his own photographic reproductions. Moved back to New York City and opened a studio in 1915. Met Duchamp in 1915, who became a lifetime friend and chessmate. Was founding member of Society of Independent Artists; *Rope Dancer Accompanies Herself with Her Shadows* was shown in the Society's first exhibition in 1917. Began series of 'aerograph' airbrush paintings in 1918 that were shown at Daniel Gallery in 1919. Established Société Anonyme with Duchamp and Katherine Dreier in 1920. Designed and edited with Duchamp the single issue of magazine *New York Dada* in 1921. Moved to Paris in 1921 with the financial support of Ferdinand Howald. First show in Paris sponsored by the Dadaists at Librarie Six, 1921. Discovered 'rayograph' process in 1922. Edition of rayograph prints, *Les Champs Délicieux*, published in 1922. Works in first international Dada show at Galerie Montaigne, 1922. Exhibited in first surrealist exhibition at Galerie Pierre in 1925. Second one-man show in Paris at Galerie Surréaliste in 1926. Made first film, *Le Retour a la Raison*, in 1923; made *Emak Bakia* in 1926, *L'Etoile de Mer* in 1928 and *Les Mystères du Chateau de Dé* in 1929. Enjoyed commercial success with portrait photographs that were visual record of haut monde in Paris in 1920's and early 1930's. One-man show of photographs at Julien Levy Gallery in New York, 1932. Album of photographs, *Man Ray Photographs*, published in U.S., 1934. Illustrated two volumes of poetry, *Facile*, 1935, and *Les Mains libres*, 1937, for his closest friend among the surrealists, poet Paul Eluard. Works appeared in Museum of Modern Art show in 1936 and in International Surrealist Exhibition at Galerie des Beaux-Arts, Paris, 1938. Returned to U.S. to live in Los Angeles in 1940. Retrospective of work at Pasadena in 1944. Married to second wife, modern dancer Juliet Browner, in 1946. Returned to Paris to live in 1951. Retrospectives at Institute of Contemporary Arts, London, 1959; Princeton University Art Museum, 1963, and Cordier and Ekstrom Gallery, New York, 1963. Autobiography, *Self Portrait*, published in London in 1963.

BIBLIOGRAPHY: Ray, Man. *Les Champs Délicieux*. Paris, 1922, preface by Tristan Tzara; Desnos, Robert. "The Work of Man Ray," *Transition*, no. 15, (Paris) 1929, pp. 264–266; Ray, Man. *Photographs, 1920–1934, Paris*. New York, 1934, texts by Breton, Eluard, Tzara; Eluard, Paul. *Facile*. Paris, 1935, photographs by Man Ray; Levy, Julien.

97 George Luks *Playing Soldiers* 1915

98 George Luks *Gossip* 1915

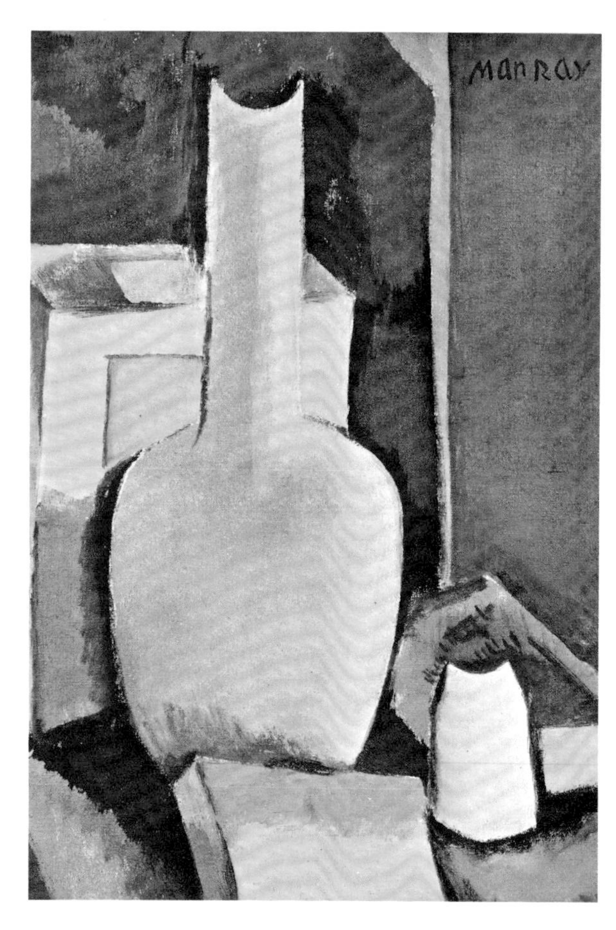

101 Man Ray *Still Life No.* 2 1913

105 Man Ray *Regatta* 1924

103 Man Ray *Madonna* 1914

104 Man Ray *Jazz* c. 1919

Surrealism. New York, 1936; Ribement-Dessaignes, George. *Man Ray.* Paris, 1924, reissued Paris, 1937; Wescher, P. "Man Ray as a Painter," *Magazine of Art*, vol. XLVI, January 1953, pp. 31–37; Waldberg, Patrick. "Bonjour Monsieur Man Ray!," *Quadrum*, no. 7, (Brussels) 1959, pp. 91–102; Alloway, Lawrence. "Some London Exhibitions: Man Made Objects," *Art International*, vol. 3, no. 4–5, 1959, p. 61; Melville, Robert. "Man Ray in London," *Arts*, vol. 33, no. 9, June 1959, pp. 45–47; Copley, William. "The Dada of Us All," *Art News*, no. 7, Winter 1963, pp. 14–23; Ray, Man. *Self Portrait.* London and Boston, 1963; Bolz, Carl. "Man Ray and N.Y. Dada," *College Art Journal*, vol. XXIII, no. 3, Spring 1964, pp. 207–213; "Man Ray: Objects of My Affection," catalogue, Galleria Schwarz, Milan, 14 March–3 April 1964, texts by Ray, Tzara; "Man Ray," catalogue, Princeton University Art Gallery, 1964, essays by Kelleher, Belz; "Man Ray," catalogue, Los Angeles County Museum of Art, 27 October–25 December 1966, texts by Langsner, Ray; "Dada, Surrealism and Their Heritage," catalogue, Museum of Modern Art, New York, 1968, text by William Rubin.

100 *Still Life No. 1.* 1913.
Oil on canvas, 18 × 24 in. (45.7 × 61 cm.).
Signed and dated lower right "Man Ray 1913."

101 *Still Life No. 2.* n.d. *
Oil on canvas, 14 × 10 in. (35.6 × 25.4 cm.).
Signed upper right "Man Ray."

102 *Still Life No. 3.* 1914.
Oil on canvas, 10⅛ × 8⅛ in. (25.7 × 20.8 cm.).
Signed and dated lower left "Man Ray 1914."

103 *Madonna.* 1914. *
Oil on canvas, 20⅛ × 16⅛ in. (51.1 × 41 cm.).
Signed lower left "Man Ray," dated in upper half of canvas "ANNO D MCMXIV."

Man Ray, the only American painter to achieve fame as a Dadaist, is a seminal figure in American art. Until 1921, when he left for Paris with the help of Ferdinand Howald, he experimented with a variety of painting and photographic techniques.

In 1914, his style shifted from romantic expressionism to flat-patterned abstractions, schematicized and subdued. From this point on, he abandoned traditional ideas of composition and "aesthetic" subject matter in order to concentrate on a redefinition of artistic possibilities.

There is a whimsical twist of the imagination in *Madonna* that prefigures the irony of Man Ray's later Dada works; he has chosen to deal with a subject whose historical and religious significance precluded its use by other modern artists.

EXHIBITIONS: Canton Art Institute, Canton, Ohio, 25 March–15 April 1956; ACA American Heritage Gallery, New York, "50th Anniversary of the Forum Exhibition," 14 March–9 April 1966, no. 27, illus.

104 *Jazz.* c. 1919. *
Air brush on paper ('aerograph'), 31 × 25 in. (78.8 × 63.6 cm.)

A technical innovator of extraordinary virtuosity, Man Ray began, around 1918, to experiment with a sprayed paint technique. He called the resulting works "aerographs." *Jazz*, one of the most intricately beautiful paintings he executed, is formally and technically original. The smooth, immaterial shapes are precociously contemporary, and are perfect vehicles for transforming the rhythm and mood of a musical abstraction into a pictorial one.

EXHIBITIONS: Cincinnati Art Museum, 1935; University of Minnesota Art Gallery, Minneapolis, Minnesota, "Music and Art," 4 April–18 May 1958; Grand Rapids Art Gallery, Grand Rapids, Michigan, 15 June–29 July 1958; Allentown Art Museum, Allentown, Pennsylvania, 1–18 April 1961; University of Iowa, Iowa City, Iowa, "American Pioneer Artists 1903–1932," 24 May–2 August 1962, no. 58, illus. p. 26; Whitney Museum, New York, "The Decade of the Armory Show, New Directions in American Art 1910–1920," 27 February–14 April 1963, no. 80, illus. p. 60; Los Angeles County Museum of Art, Los Angeles, California, "Man Ray," 27 October–25 December 1966, no. 30; Grand Rapids Art Museum, Grand Rapids, Michigan, "20th Century American Paintings," 1–30 April 1967.

REPRODUCED: Brown, Milton. *American Painting from the Armory Show to the Depression.* Princeton, 1955. p. 105; Goodrich, Lloyd. *Pioneers of Modern Art in America; the Decade of the Armory Show, 1910–1920.* New York, 1963, p. 60.

105 *Regatta.* 1924. *
Oil on canvas, 19⅝ × 23⅞ in. (50 × 60.7 cm.).
Signed and dated lower right "Man Ray 1924."

EXHIBITIONS: Cincinnati Art Museum, 1935; Carnegie Institute, 1952.

106 *Le Grand Palais.* c. 1922–1926.
Oil on canvas, 19⅝ × 23⅞ in. (50 × 60.7 cm.).

Edward Middleton Manigault (1887–1922)

Born in 1887. Was member of an old Huguenot family from Charleston, South Carolina. Lived in New York City most of his life. First show of his works in New York in 1909. Exhibited regularly at Daniel Gallery and Montross Gallery, New York, after 1909. Married Gertrude Buffington Phillips in 1915, the year he volunteered for the World War I British Expeditionary Forces. He was gassed and sent home the same year. War injuries left him in poor health until his death. Was close friend and pupil of Kenneth Hayes Miller in New York. Around 1919, he abandoned fantastic themes to paint cubist works that he later destroyed. He moved to San Francisco in 1919, where he died in 1922 as a result of self-imposed starvation to which he subjected himself because he believed it enabled him to see new colors previously invisible to him.

BIBLIOGRAPHY: *New York Times*, obituary, 6 September 1922, p. 15, and 7 September 1922, p. 19; "Paintings by E. Middleton Manigault," catalogue, Norton Gallery of Art, West Palm Beach, Florida, 29 November–8 December 1963.

107 *Procession*. 1911. *
Oil on canvas, 20 × 24 in. (50.7 × 61 cm.).
Signed and dated lower right "Manigault 1911."

Manigault, about whom little is known, was a romantic and visionary painter whose work is related to that of Davies and Eilshemius. Although his landscapes were most often peopled with eccentric, idyllically erotic figures, an atmosphere of fantasy and sumptuousness also characterizes his more prosaic subjects. In *Procession*, the stately rhythms and layered composition, covered by a filigree of branches, provide an over-all texture that is reminiscent of Persian tapestries. Manigault's exotic, personal style remains one of the highlights of American painting in the early decades of the century.

EXHIBITIONS: Daniel Gallery, New York, "Manigault Exhibition," September 1914, no. 3.

REPRODUCED: *The Arts*, vol. 8, August 1925, p. 79; Pierson, William H., Jr. and Martha Davidson (ed.). *Arts of the United States: A Pictorial Survey*. New York, 1960, p. 351, no. 3249.

John Marin (1870–1953)

Born Rutherford, New Jersey in 1870. Raised in New Jersey and Delaware. Began drawing in early childhood. Attended Stevens Institute of Technology for one year. Held odd jobs, then worked for four years in an architect's office. Produced first water colors in 1888. From 1893 to 1899 he painted and sketched, taking occasional, free-lance drafting assignments from architects. Studied at the Pennsylvania Academy of Fine Arts, Philadelphia, with Thomas Anshutz and Hugh Breckenridge from 1899 until around 1903. Won Academy prize in 1900 for sketches done independently in New Jersey. Studied one year at Art Students League in New York City with Frank Vincent DuMond in 1904. Went to Europe in 1905 and settled in Paris. Did etchings from 1905 to 1910, which were influenced by Whistler and the French engraver, Charles Meryon. Travelled in the Netherlands and Belgium in 1906 and in 1908, and Italy in 1907. *The Mills of Meaux* purchased by Luxembourg Museum in 1908. Exhibited in Salon d'Automne, 1908. Oil paintings shown in Salon des Indépendents in 1909. Met Edward Steichen in 1909 who brought Marin's paintings to Stieglitz' attention. Marin's water colors were shown, with works by Alfred Maurer, at Stieglitz' Gallery of the Photo-Secession in March 1909. Marin returned to New York in December, 1909. First one-man show held at "291" gallery in February 1910; one-man shows there in 1913 and 1915. Went to Europe in 1910 to paint in the Tyrol. Came back to U.S. in 1911. Ten water colors he left behind in Paris were shown at the Salon d'Automne, 1911. Marin first saw works by Cézanne at Stieglitz' gallery that year. He lived in New York City until 1916 when he moved to Cliffside, New Jersey. Spent his summers painting, primarily in Maine, upstate New York and Massachusetts. Works shown in Armory Show in 1913 and in the Forum Exhibition of 1916. Director of Society of Independent Artists in 1917. Retrospective exhibition at Daniel Gallery in 1920. Exhibited at Montross Gallery and the Intimate Gallery in the 1920's. Showed annually at An American Place gallery from 1929 to 1950, then at the Downtown Gallery until 1953. Retrospectives at Museum of Modern Art, New York, in 1936; in Washington, D.C., Boston and Minneapolis, in 1947; and in Los Angeles in 1949. Summers of 1929 and 1930 spent in New Mexico, where he visited Stieglitz and Georgia O'Keeffe. He died in Cape Split, Maine, October, 1953.

BIBLIOGRAPHY: Gallatin, Albert Eugene. *American Water Colorists*. New York, 1922; Marin, John. "John Marin, by Himself," *Creative Art*, vol. III, October 1928, pp. xxxv–xxxix; Benson, E. M. *John Marin: The Man and his Work*. Washington, D.C., 1935; "John Marin: Water Colors, Oil Paintings, Etchings," catalogue, Museum of Modern Art, New York, 21 October–22 November 1936, preface by Alfred H. Barr, Jr., essays by McBride, Hartley, Benson; Josephson, M. "Leprechaun on the Palisades," *New Yorker*, vol. 18, March 1942, pp. 26–35; "John Marin, A Retrospective Exhibition," catalogue, Institute of Contemporary Art, Boston, 1947, forward by Plaut, essays by Helm, Wight; Helm, MacKinley. *John Marin*. New York and Boston, 1948; Mellquist, Jerome. "John Marin: Painter of Specimen Days," *American Artist*, vol. 13, no. 7, issue 27, September 1949, pp. 56–59, 67–69; Norman, Dorothy (ed.). *Selected Writings of John Marin*. New York, 1949; Finkelstein, Louis. "Marin and de Kooning," *Magazine of Art*, vol. 43, no. 6, October 1950, pp. 202–206; Rosenblum, Robert. "Marin's Dynamism," *Art Digest*, no. 28, February 1954, p. 13; Soby, James Thrall. "The Paintings of John Marin," *Perspectives U.S.A.*, no. 11, 1955, pp. 48–53; Norman, Dorothy. "Conversations and Notes," *College Art Journal*, vol. XIV, no. 4, Summer 1955, pp. 320–331; "John Marin Memorial Exhibition," catalogue, University of California, Berkeley and Los Angeles, 1956, essays

107 Edward Middleton Manigault *Procession* 1911

108 John Marin *Tyrolean Mountains* 1910

by Helm, Wight; Newhall, Beaumont. "A Day with John Marin," *Art in America*, vol. 51, no. 4, August 1963, pp. 107–111.

108 *Tyrolean Mountains*. 1910. *
Water color, 14½ × 17¾ in. (36.9 × 45 cm.).
Signed and dated lower left "Marin 10."

In 1910, John Marin joined Alfred Stieglitz' "291," the most radical gallery on the American art scene at the beginning of the 20th century. Along with the works of Arthur Dove, Georgia O'Keeffe and Marsden Hartley who also exhibited at "291," Marin's paintings heralded a truly American modernism.

Marin was an individualist who developed a highly personal system of abbreviation to communicate his vision of nature. His work was never abstract because it always referred to real objects; if anything, he preferred to be called a lyrical realist.

Tyrolean Mountains is remarkable for an intensity rarely achieved in so limpid a medium. With a light touch and economy of means, Marin was able, like the old Chinese masters, to create transparency and weightlessness while retaining a vital exuberance.

EXHIBITIONS: Cincinnati Art Museum, 1935; Arts Club of Chicago, 1939, no. 16; Allen Memorial Art Museum, Oberlin College, Oberlin, Ohio, 7–29 January 1941; University Gallery, University of Minnesota, Minneapolis, Minnesota, December, 1942; John Herron Art Institute, Indianapolis, Indiana, "Five Water Colors by American Artists," 1 February–8 March 1944; Indiana University Museum of Art, Bloomington, Indiana, 10–25 March 1944; American Federation of Arts, New York, "Early 20th Century American Water Colors," circulating exhibition, 1 August 1948–1 June 1949; Taft Museum, Cincinnati, Ohio, "The Cincinnati Biennial: Festival of the Arts," 27 January–18 March 1951; University of Nebraska Art Galleries, Lincoln, Nebraska, 11 January–10 February 1952; Norfolk Museum, Norfolk, Virginia, "Significant American Moderns," March–April 1953; Museum of Fine Arts of Houston, Houston, Texas, "John Marin Memorial Exhibition," 29 November 1953–3 January 1954, no. 8; Philbrook Art Center, 1956; Isaac Delgado Museum of Art, New Orleans, Louisiana, "1910–1960, A 50th Anniversary Exhibition," 15 November 1960–1 January 1961, no. 77; Allentown Art Museum, Allentown, Pennsylvania, 1–18 April 1961.

REPRODUCED: Brown, Milton. *American Painting from the Armory Show to the Depression*. Princeton, 1955, p. 40.

109 *Summer Foliage*. 1913.
Water color, 15⅝ × 18½ in. (39.4 × 47 cm.).
Signed and dated lower right "Marin 13."

110 *Seaside, An Interpretation*. 1914. *
Water color, 15½ × 18⅝ in. (39.4 × 47.1 cm.).
Signed and dated lower left "Marin 14."

EXHIBITIONS: Allen Memorial Art Museum, Oberlin College, Oberlin, Ohio, 7–29 January 1941; National Gallery of Fine Art, Inter-American Office, Washington, D.C. (prepared by the Walker Art Center, Minneapolis, Minnesota), "A Survey of Water Color—U.S.A., From 1870–1946," circulating exhibition to Central and South America, 1946; Cincinnati Art Museum, Cincinnati, Ohio, "An American Show," 1 October–5 November 1948, no. 61; 25th Biennale di Venezia, 1950, no. 33, p. 378; Carnegie Institute, 1952; Museum of Fine Arts of Houston, Houston, Texas, "John Marin Memorial Exhibition," 29 November 1953–3 January 1954, no. 2; American Federation of Arts, New York, "Adventures in Collecting," October 1958–October 1960; University of Arizona Art Gallery, Tucson, Arizona, "John Marin Exhibition," 9 February–10 March 1963, illus.; Indiana University Museum of Art, Bloomington, Indiana, "American Painting 1910–1960," 19 April–10 May 1964, no. 46, illus.

REPRODUCED: Benson, E. M. *John Marin*. American Federation of Arts, 1935, pl. 13, opposite p. 32 (titled *Looking out on Casco Bay*); *American Magazine of Art*, vol. 28, October 1935, p. 604.

111 *The Coast*. 1914. *
Water color, 15½ × 18½ in. (39.4 × 47 cm.).
Signed and dated lower right "Marin 14."

EXHIBITIONS: Cincinnati Art Museum, 1935; Allen Memorial Art Museum, Oberlin College, Oberlin, Ohio, 7–29 January 1941; Colorado Springs Fine Arts Center, Colorado Springs, Colorado, "Exhibition of Water Colors: Homer, Sargent, Marin," 18 April–11 June 1947, no. 42; Taft Museum, Cincinnati, Ohio, "The Cincinnati Biennial: Festival of the Arts," 27 January–18 March 1951; Art Gallery, University of Miami, Florida, "John Marin," 2–23 October 1951, no. 6; American Federation of Arts, New York, "John Marin, Milestonesand Masterpieces in Water Color,"1951; Museum of Fine Arts of Houston, Houston, Texas, "John Marin Memorial Exhibition," 29 November 1953–3 January 1954, no. 3; Philbrook Art Center, 1956; American Federation of Arts, New York, "Adventures in Collecting," October 1958–October 1960; University of Arizona Art Gallery, Tucson, Arizona, "John Marin Retrospective Exhibition," 9 February–10 March 1963.

112 *Big Wood Island*. 1914.
Water color, 13⅞ × 15⅞ in. (35.2 × 40.3 cm.).
Signed and dated lower right "Marin 14."

113 *Landscape*. 1914.
Water color, 18⅝ × 16¼ in. (47.3 × 41.2 cm.).
Signed and dated lower left "Marin 14."

114 *The Violet Lake*. 1915.
Water color, 15½ × 18⅝ in. (39.4 × 47.2 cm.).
Signed and dated lower left "Marin 15."

115 *Delaware River Country*. 1916. *
Water color, 15⅞ × 18¾ in. (40.3 × 47.6 cm.).
Signed and dated lower right "Marin 16."

116 *Breakers, Maine Coast*. 1917. *
Water color, 15⅞ × 18⅝ in. (40.3 × 47.2 cm.).
Signed and dated lower right "Marin 17."

After 1910, Marin's water colors acquired a tense, brittle quality that conveyed more effectively the conflict and dynamism he felt in nature. In *Breakers, Maine Coast,* the washes of color and nervous, emphatic lines produce an explosive sensation.

Marin's habit of painting with both hands at the same time may be partially responsible for the singular freshness, freedom and energy of his work.

EXHIBITIONS: Cincinnati Art Museum, 1935; Arts Club of Chicago, 1939, no. 19; Allen Memorial Art Museum, Oberlin College, Oberlin, Ohio, 7–29 January 1941; University of Nebraska Art Galleries, Lincoln, Nebraska, 11 January–10 February 1952; Carnegie Institute, 1952; Museum of Fine Arts of Houston, Houston, Texas, "John Marin Memorial Exhibition," 29 November 1963–3 January 1954, no. 5; Ohio University, Athens, Ohio, "American Painting 1804–1954," 1 May–15 June 1954, no. 29, illus.; Philbrook Art Center, 1956; Albany Institute, 1958; American Federation of Arts, New York, "Adventures in Collecting," October 1958–October 1960; Museum of Modern Art, New York, "The Stieglitz Circle," circulating loan exhibition, February 1962–January 1964; Colby College, Waterville, Maine, "Maine: 100 Artists of the Twentieth Century," 25 January–30 September 1964, circulated by American Federation of Arts, December 1964–December 1966, illus. p. 13.

REPRODUCED: Seiberling, Frank. *Looking into Art*. New York, 1959, p. 158.

117 *Sand Dunes*. 1917.
Water color, 18⅞ × 15⅞ in. (47.8 × 40.3 cm.).
Signed and dated lower left "Marin 17."

118 *The Cove*. 1917.
Water color, 16 × 19 in. (40.6 × 48.2 cm.).
Signed and dated lower right "Marin 17."

119 *The Grey Sea*. 1917. *
Water color, 19⅛ × 15⅞ in. (48.5 × 40.3 cm.).
Signed lower left "Marin 17."

EXHIBITIONS: Arts Club of Chicago, 1939, no. 18; Carnegie Institute, 1952; Art Galleries, University of California, "John Marin Memorial Exhibition," circulated to Cleveland Museum of Art; Minneapolis Institute of Arts; Museum of Fine Arts, Boston; Phillips Memorial Gallery, Washington; San Francisco Museum of Art; 1955, no. 10; Society of the Four Arts, Palm Beach, Florida, "John Marin Memorial Exhibition," 9–20 March 1956, no. 23; Smithsonian Institution, Washington, D.C., travelling exhibition to Arts Council Gallery, London, "John Marin, Paintings, Water Colours, Drawings, Etchings," 22 September–20 October 1956, no. 42.

120 *The Shore*. 1917.
Water color, 15⅝ × 18⅝ in. (39.7 × 47.2 cm.).
Signed and dated lower right "Marin 17."

121 *Study of the Sea*. 1917.
Water color, 16 × 19 in. (40.6 × 48.2 cm.).
Signed and dated lower right "Marin 17."

122 *From the Ocean*. 1919. *
Water color, 16⅛ × 19 in. (41 × 48.2 cm.).
Signed and dated lower left "Marin 19."

Marin's more tranquil landscapes, such as *From the Ocean*, resemble those of Cézanne. Like the French master, he had a strong sense of internal construction; however, unlike Cézanne, Marin was interested in eliciting atmosphere rather than form, spontaneity rather than structure.

Marin maintained that he did not become aware of Cézanne until 1911 after his own personal style had crystallized; thus the similarities between the work of Marin and Cézanne indicate a shared sensibility instead of any direct influence.

EXHIBITIONS: Daniel Gallery, New York, "Exhibition of Water Colors by John Marin," April 1920, no. 1; Arts Club of Chicago, 1939; Allen Memorial Art Museum, Oberlin College, Oberlin, Ohio, 7–29 January 1941; American Federation of Arts, New York, "Early 20th Century American Water Colors," circulating exhibition, 1 August 1948–1 June 1949; Carnegie Institute, 1952; American Federation of Arts, New York, "Pioneers of American Abstract Art," circulating exhibition, December 1955–January 1957, no. 21; Rose Fried Gallery, New York, 19 December 1956–9 January 1957; Albany Institute, 1958; American Federation of Arts, New York, "Adventures in Collecting," October 1958–October 1960; Allentown Art Museum, Allentown, Pennsylvania, 1–18 April 1961.

123 *Sea Blue Effect*. 1919.
Water color, 16⅛ × 19¼ in. (40.8 × 48.6 cm.).
Signed and dated lower left "Marin 19."

110 John Marin *Seaside, An Interpretation* 1914

111 John Marin *The Coast* 1914

115 John Marin *Delaware River Country* 1916

116 John Marin *Breakers, Maine Coast* 1917

119 John Marin *The Grey Sea* 1917

124 John Marin *Sunset, Maine Coast* 1919

122 John Marin *From the Ocean* 1919

127 John Marin *Off Stonington* 1921

124 *Sunset, Maine Coast*. 1919. *
Water color, 16¼ × 19¼ in. (41.3 × 49.0 cm.).

EXHIBITIONS: Cincinnati Art Museum, 1935; Allen Memorial Art Museum, Oberlin, Ohio, 7–29 January 1941; Colorado Springs Fine Arts Center, Colorado Springs, Colorado, "Exhibition of Water Colors: Homer, Sargent, Marin," 18 April–11 June 1947, no. 43; Norton Gallery of Art, West Palm Beach, Florida, "Masters of Water Colors, Marin, Demuth and Prendergast," 3–26 February 1950; American Federation of Arts, New York, "American Pioneers of Abstract Art," circulating exhibition, December 1955–January 1957; American Federation of Arts, New York, "Adventures in Collecting," October 1958–October 1960; Museum of Modern Art, New York, "The Stieglitz Circle," circulating loan exhibition, February 1962–January 1964, no. 2; Montclair Art Museum, Montclair, New Jersey, "John Marin—America's Modern Pioneer," 23 February–29 March 1964, no. 13.

REPRODUCED: Benson, E. M. *John Marin*. American Federation of Arts, 1935. pl. 17 opposite p. 40; *American Magazine of Art*, vol. 28, October 1935, p. 606.

125 *Red Sun*. 1919.
Water color, 16⅛ × 19 in. (40.9 × 48.4 cm.).
Signed and dated lower left "Marin 19."

126 *Autumn*. 1919.
Water color, 19 × 16⅛ in. (48.2 × 41 cm.).
Signed and dated lower left "Marin 19."

127 *Off Stonington*. 1921. *
Water color, 16⅜ × 19½ in. (41.4 × 49.5 cm.).
Signed and dated lower right "Marin 21."

Marin's paintings have been called experiences in time. In *Off Stonington*, the surging washes superimposed on planes of color evoke the rhythm and swell of the sea. Dramatic tension is created by a device Marin often employed, the incorporation of intense passages of movement within the framework of a balanced, centered composition.

EXHIBITIONS: Montross Gallery, New York, "Recent Pictures by John Marin, 1922–23," 6–24 March 1923, no. 12; Museum of Living Art, New York University, New York, "Opening Exhibition," 13 December 1927–25 January 1928; Cleveland Museum of Art, Cleveland, Ohio, "American Painting from 1860 until Today," 23 June–4 October 1937, no. 144; University Gallery, University of Minnesota, Minneapolis, Minnesota, December 1942; John Herron Art Institute, Indianapolis, Indiana, "Water Colors by American Artists," 1 February–8 March 1944; Indiana University, Bloomington, Indiana, 10–25 March 1944; National Gallery of Fine Art, Inter-American office, Washington, D.C. (prepared by the Walker Art Center, Minneapolis), "A Survey of Water Color—U.S.A., from 1870–1946," circulating exhibition to Central and South America, 1946; American Federation of Arts, New York, "Early 20th Century American Water Colors," circulating exhibition, 1 August 1948–1 June 1949; 25th Biennale di Venezia, 1950, no. 37, p. 378; Carnegie Institute, 1952; Museum of Fine Arts of Houston, Houston, Texas, "John Marin Memorial Exhibition," 29 November 1953–3 January 1954, no. 10; Marquette University, Marquette, Wisconsin, "Festival of American Arts," 20 April–20 May 1956; Contemporary Arts Center of Cincinnati Art Museum and Dayton Art Institute, Ohio, "An American Viewpoint, Realism in the Twentieth Century," 10 October 1957–15 January 1958; Ohio Wesleyan University, Delaware, Ohio, 19 November–13 December 1959; Colby College, Waterville, Maine, "100 Artists of the 20th Century," 25 June–30 September 1964, circulated by American Federation of Arts, December 1964–December 1966, no. 37.

REPRODUCED: *Arts*, vol. 8, August 1925, p. 85.

128 *Off York Island*. 1922.
Water color, 17¼ × 20⅛ in. (43.8 × 51 cm.).
Signed and dated lower right "Marin 22."

129 *Sail Boat in Harbor*. c. 1922. *
Water color, 19¼ × 16 in. (48.5 × 40.5 cm.).

In *Sail Boat in Harbor*, the characteristic energy of Marin's paintings is reinforced by arbitrary lines of force superimposed on the sky and sea.

EXHIBITIONS: Museum of Living Art, New York University, New York, "Opening Exhibition," 13 December 1927–25 January 1928; Museum of Modern Art, New York, "Paintings by Nineteen Living Americans," 13 December 1929–12 January 1930, no. 63 (titled *Sailboat from Cliff*); Arts Club of Chicago, 1939, no. 22 (titled *Red Lightning*); Fine Arts Gallery, San Diego, California, "Water Colors of an Earlier Day," 23 June–1 September 1941, no. 24; University Gallery, University of Minnesota, Minneapolis, Minnesota, December 1942; John Herron Art Institute, Indianapolis, Indiana, "Water Colors by American Artists," February–March 1944; Indiana University, Bloomington, Indiana, 10–25 March 1944; Colorado Springs Fine Arts Center, Colorado Springs, Colorado, "Exhibition of Water Colors, Homer, Sargent, Marin," 18 April–11 June 1947, no. 44; Cincinnati Art Museum, Cincinnati, Ohio, "An American Show," 1 October–5 November 1948, no. 73; 25th Biennale di Venezia, 1950, no. 40, p. 378; Carnegie Institute, 1952; Museum of Fine Arts of Houston, Houston, Texas, "John Marin Memorial Exhibition," 29 November 1953–3 January 1954, no. 7; American Federation of Arts, New York, "A.F.A. Exhibition in France," April 1954–February 1955.

130 *A Study on Sand Island*. 1922. *
Water color, 14⅛ × 17 in. (35.8 × 43 cm.).
Signed and dated lower right "Marin 22."

EXHIBITIONS: Allen Memorial Art Museum, Oberlin College, Oberlin, Ohio, 7–29 January 1941; Colorado Springs Fine Arts Center, Colorado Springs, Colorado, "Exhibition of Water Colors, Homer, Sargent, Marin," 18 April–11 June 1947, no. 45; Philbrook Art Center, 1956; American Federation of Arts, New York, "Adventures in Collecting," October 1958–October 1960.

131 *Palisades, No. 1.* 1922.
Water color, 16 × 19⅛ in. (40.7 × 48.6 cm.).
Signed and dated lower left "Marin 22."

132 *Palisades, No. 2.* 1922. *
Water color, 16 × 19⅛ in. (40.7 × 48.6 cm.).
Signed and dated lower right "Marin 22."

EXHIBITIONS: Colorado Springs Fine Arts Center, Colorado Springs, Colorado, "Exhibition of Water Colors, Homer, Sargent, Marin," 18 April–11 June 1947, no. 46; Cincinnati Art Museum, Cincinnati, Ohio, "An American Show," 1 October–5 November 1948, no. 70; Museum of Fine Arts of Houston, Texas, "John Marin Memorial Exhibition," 29 November 1953–3 January 1954, no. 9; Philbrook Art Center, 1956; Corcoran Memorial Gallery, Washington, D.C. "The New Tradition," 27 April–2 June 1963, no. 65; Montclair Art Museum, Montclair, New Jersey, "John Marin —America's Modern Pioneer," 23 February–29 March 1964, no. 16.

133 *A Piece of Stonington.* 1922.
Water color, 14⅝ × 17¼ in. (37.2 × 43.8 cm.).
Signed and dated lower right "Marin 22."

134 *Ship, Sea and Sky Forms, An Impression.* 1923. *
Water color, 13½ × 17 in. (34.3 × 43.2 cm.).
Signed and dated lower right "Marin 23."

Marin attempted to bring nature close to himself and to those who viewed his work. The more familiar he became with his subject matter, the more he simplified. In *Ship, Sea and Sky Forms*, real objects are barely sketched-in to achieve what Marin called "an impression." The interior framing lines, which he used in several pictures of this period, are as strong as the depicted objects, creating tension between the two.

EXHIBITIONS: Cincinnati Art Museum, 1935; Museum of Modern Art, New York, "John Marin," 21 October–22 November 1936, no. 56; Cleveland Museum of Art, Cleveland, Ohio, "American Painting from 1860 until Today," 23 June–4 October 1937, no. 141, p. 34; Horace Rackham School of Graduate Studies, University of Michigan, Ann Arbor, Michigan, "American Painting," 1–31 July 1940, no. 38; Allen Memorial Art Museum, Oberlin, Ohio, 7–29 January 1941; John Herron Institute, "Watercolors by American Artists," 1 February–8 March 1944; Indiana University, Bloomington, Indiana, 10–25 March 1944; American Federation of Arts, New York (sponsored by the Whitney Museum), "A History of American Water Color Painting," 1946; Cincinnati Art Museum, Cincinnati, Ohio," An American Show," 1 October–5 November 1948, no. 64; Norton Gallery of Art, West Palm Beach, Florida, "Masters of Watercolor—Marin, Demuth and Prendergast," 3–26 February 1950, no. 2; Munson-Williams-Proctor Institute, Utica, New York, "John Marin, Water Colors, Oils, Prints and Drawings," 2–30 December 1951, no. 7; Carnegie Institute, 1952; Museum of Fine Arts of Houston, Houston, Texas, "John Marin Memorial Exhibition," 29 November 1953–3 January 1954, no. 1, illus.; American Federation of Arts, New York, "AFA Exhibition in France," April 1954–February 1955; Philbrook Art Center, 1956; Davison Art Center, Wesleyan University, Middletown, Connecticut, "America Seen," 15 September–10 October 1957; Albany Institute, 1958; American Federation of Arts, New York, "Adventures in Collecting," October 1958–October 1960; Allentown Art Museum, Allentown, Pennsylvania, 1–18 April 1961; Indiana University Museum of Art, Indiana University, Bloomington, Indiana, "American Painting 1910 to 1960," 19 April–10 May 1964, no. 47, illus.

REPRODUCED: *Arts*, vol. 8, August 1925, p. 93; *Formes*, no. 21, January 1932, opposite p. 196 (titled *An Impression*); Benson, E. M. *John Marin.* American Federation of Arts, 1935, pl. 3, opposite p. 16; *American Magazine of Art*, vol. 28, October 1935, frontispiece; Rigg, Margaret. "Truth as the Artist Sees It," *Motive*, May 1955, p. 22.

135 *Impression.* 1923. *
Water color, 18½ × 21¼ in. (44.4 × 54 cm.).
Signed and dated lower right "Marin 23."

EXHIBITIONS: Arts Club of Chicago, 1939, no. 25; University Gallery, University of Minnesota, Minneapolis, Minnesota, December 1942; 25th Biennale di Venezia, 1950, no. 41, p. 379; American Federation of Arts, New York, "AFA Exhibition in France," April 1954–February 1955; Allentown Art Museum, Allentown, Pennsylvania, 1–18 April 1961.

Henry Lee McFee (1886–1953)

Born St. Louis, Missouri, 1886. Studied painting at St. Louis School of Fine Arts and at Stevenson Art School in Pittsburgh in 1907. Moved to Woodstock, New York, in 1908 where he studied landscape painting under Birge Harrison. Remained in Woodstock and helped found art colony there. Exhibited with the 'Post Impressionists' group at the McDowell Club in New York, 1912, and in the Forum Exhibition in New York

129 John Marin *Ship, Sea and Sky Forms, An Impression* 1923

132 John Marin *Palisades No.* 2 1922

135 John Marin *Impression* 1923

130 John Marin *A Study on Sand Island* 1922

134 John Marin *Sail Boat in Harbor* c. 1922

136 Henry Lee McFee *Still Life* 1916

137 Kenneth Hayes Miller *Recumbent Figure* 1910–1911

138 Jerome Myers *An Interlude* 1916

142 Maurice Brazil Prendergast *Outskirts of Village* n.d.

144 Maurice Brazil Prendergast *South Side Hills* n.d.

1916. Works shown by Frank K. M. Rehn Gallery in 1950's. Artist in residence at Scripps College, Claremont, California, in 1950. Died in Los Angeles in 1953.

BIBLIOGRAPHY: Brook, Alexander. "Henry Lee McFee," *The Arts*, vol. 4, 1923, pp. 251–261; McFee, Henry Lee. "My Painting and Its Development," *Creative Arts*, vol. 4, no. 3, March 1929, pp. xxix–xxxi; Barker, Virgil. *Henry Lee McFee*. American Artists Group, New York, 1931; Miller, Arthur. *Henry Lee McFee*. Scripps College, Claremont, California, 1950.

136 *Still Life*. 1916. *
Oil on canvas, 20 × 16 in. (50.7 × 40.6 cm.).
Signed and dated lower left "McFee 1916."

McFee's mature style dates from 1916, when he showed eight paintings in the *Forum* exhibition. Although he did not travel abroad until 1921, he was familiar with the work of Cézanne and the Cubists through reproductions and exhibitions at Stieglitz' "291" gallery.

In *Still Life*, the stress is on color modulation and elegant composition. McFee felt that the spaces in a painting were as important as the objects represented, and a constantly shifting relationship between the two becomes the focal point of this work.

EXHIBITIONS: Dayton Art Institute, 1941; Whitney Museum, New York, "Pioneers of Modern Art in America," 9 April–19 May 1946, circulated by American Federation of Arts, 1946–1947, no. 103, illus.; Brooklyn Museum, Brooklyn, New York, "Revolution and Tradition," 15 November 1951–6 January 1952, no. 27, p. 8; Ohio Wesleyan University, Delaware, Ohio, 19 November–13 December 1959; ACA American Heritage Gallery, New York, "50th Anniversary of the Forum Exhibition," 14 March–9 April 1966, no. 22, illus.

REPRODUCED: *Arts*, vol. 8, August 1925, p. 72; Baur, John I. H. *Revolution and Tradition in Modern American Art*. Cambridge, 1951, no. 128.

Kenneth Hayes Miller (1876–1952)

Born Oneida, New York, 1876. Began studies at Art Students League, New York, in early 1890's under H. Siddons Mowbray, Kenyon Cox, F. Luis Mora and Frank V. DuMond. Later studied at the New York School with William Merritt Chase. Visited Europe in 1900 and upon returning to New York that year began teaching at New York School where he remained until 1911. Taught at the Art Students League from 1911 until 1936 and again from 1944 to 1951. Among his students were Hartley, Kuniyoshi, Spencer, Hopper, Bellows, Kent and Manigault. Maintained a studio on East 14th Street for most of his painting career. Four of his paintings were shown in the Armory Show, 1913. Was a close friend of Albert Pinkham Ryder. Had one-man show at Montross Gallery, New York, in 1922 and 1925, and at Rehn Gallery in 1929, 1935 and 1938. Retrospective exhibition held at Art Students League in 1949. Died in 1952.

BIBLIOGRAPHY: Burroughs, Alan. "Kenneth Hayes Miller," *Arts*, vol. XIV, no. 6, December 1928, pp. 300–307; Goodrich, Lloyd. *Kenneth Hayes Miller*. New York, 1930; Burroughs, Alan. *Kenneth Hayes Miller*. American Artists Group, New York, 1931; Salpeter, Harry; "Kenneth Hayes Miller, Intellectual," *Esquire*, October 1937, p. 89.

137 *Recumbent Figure*. 1910–1911. *
Oil on paper-covered panel, 12½ × 16⅝ in. (31.7 × 42.2 cm.).
Signed lower left "Hayes Miller."

Miller, a close friend of Albert Pinkham Ryder, was influenced by the older artist's brooding and romantic vision. This painting, shown at the New York Armory Show of 1913, combines Ryder's melancholic flavor with a monumental form whose antecedents are to be found in the colossal grotesques of Goya.

EXHIBITIONS: Association of American Painters and Sculptors, New York, "The Armory Show," 17 February–15 March 1913; Dayton Art Institute, 1941; Munson-Williams-Proctor Institute, Utica, New York, "Armory Show, Fiftieth Anniversary," 17 February–28 April 1963; National Academy of Design, sponsored by the Art Students League, New York, "Kenneth Hayes Miller, A Memorial Exhibition," 23 September–11 October 1963, no. 5.

REPRODUCED: Brown, Milton W. *The Story of The Armory Show*. New York, 1963, no. 51, p. 270.

Jerome Myers (1867–1940)

Born Petersburg, Virginia, 1867. Grew up in Philadelphia. Moved to New York City at age of eighteen, where he remained until his death. Studied at Cooper Union and at the Art Students League. Lower East Side of New York was his favorite subject matter, so he rarely left the city. He did travel abroad briefly in 1896. Began working in oils after age forty. First one-man show in 1908. Involved in early stages of planning for Armory Show of 1913. Was an associate member of National Academy of Design, where he exhibited in 1925. Died in New York in 1940.

BIBLIOGRAPHY: DuBois, Guy Pène. "Jerome Myers," *Art and Progress*, vol. V, January 1914, pp. 88–94; Phillips, Duncan. "Jerome Myers," *American Magazine of Art*, vol. VIII, October 1917, pp. 481–485; "Jerome Myers and Ernest

Lawson," *Arts and Decoration*, vol. X, March 1919, pp. 257–259; Myers, Jerome. *Artist in Manhattan.* American Artists Group, New York, 1940; "Jerome Myers," catalogue, Whitney Museum, New York, 22 April–29 May 1941, text by Harry Wickey; "Jerome Myers Memorial Exhibition," catalogue, Richmond Museum of Fine Arts, 26 January–27 February 1942; "Jerome Myers, An Artist in Manhattan," catalogue, Wilmington Society of Fine Arts, 13 January–19 February 1967.

138 *An Interlude.* 1916. *
Oil on canvas, 18 × 24 in. (45.7 × 60.7 cm.).
Signed and dated lower right "Jerome Myers, 1916 N.Y."
REPRODUCED: *Arts*, vol. 8, August 1925, p. 78.

Maurice Brazil Prendergast (1859–1924)

Born St. John's, Newfoundland, 1859. Moved to Boston in 1861. Worked for dry goods firm and then lettered show cards for a living. Made his first trip to Europe during 1886, visiting England and possibly Paris. Returned to Boston to save enough for a second trip in 1891. This time, he remained in France until 1894, studying in Paris at the Académie Colarossi with Courtois and at the Académie Julian with Jean Paul Laurens, Blanc and Constant; spent the summers in Dieppe, St. Malo and Dinard. Became a close friend of the Canadian painter James Wilson Morrice, who influenced him profoundly. Several sketches published in *The Studio*, London, in 1893. Returned to Massachusetts in 1894. Painted in and around Boston and ran a frame shop with his brother, Charles, until 1897. Illustrated Barrie's *My Lady Nicotine*, published 1896 in Boston. Took next trip to Europe from 1898 to 1899, painting in Rome the first winter, then in Venice for six months Where he discovered the Renaissance painter Carpaccio; also visited Siena, Capri, Paris and St. Malo. Works shown in joint exhibition at Art Institute of Chicago, 1900. Exhibited in 1901 at the Macbeth Gallery, New York, and at the Cincinnati Museum where his colored monotypes were shown. Began painting in water color that year. Works shown in group exhibition at Kimball Gallery, Boston, 1905. Visited New York frequently where he met William Glackens and other artists who became part of *The Eight*, after their group exhibition at Macbeth Gallery in 1908. Went to France in 1909 to paint in Paris and St. Malo. Returned to U.S. in 1910. Exhibited at Copley Gallery, Boston, in 1911. Went to Venice with his brother in 1911–1912. Exhibited at Union League Club and Cosmopolitan Club, New York, 1912. Painted in New Hampshire and joined Association of American Painters and Sculptors that year. Works shown in Armory Show, 1913. Habitually reworked his oils for long periods, making them difficult to date. Took sixth, final trip to Europe in 1914. Upon returning in the same year, he and his brother moved to New York and opened a studio together on Washington Square. Spent summers until 1922 painting in New England. Panel paintings by Prendergast, Walt Kuhn and Arthur B. Davies shown at Montross Gallery in 1915; works also exhibited at Brummer Gallery, New York, that year. Exhibited with William Glackens and John Marin at Bourgeois Gallery, New York, in 1917. Nearly deaf and in poor health after 1922, he died in New York in 1924.

BIBLIOGRAPHY Phillips, Duncan. "Prendergast," *Arts*, vol. 5, 1924, pp. 125–131; Milliken, William M. "Maurice Prendergast, American Artist," *Arts*, vol. 9, 1926, pp. 181–192; Breuning, Margaret. *Maurice Prendergast.* New York 1931; "The Prendergasts: Retrospective Exhibition of the Work of Maurice and Charles Prendergast," catalogue, Phillips Academy and Addison Gallery of American Art, 1938, essay by Van Wyck Brooks; "Four Boston Masters," catalogue, Wellesley College, Jewett Arts Center and Boston Museum of Fine Arts, April–June 1959; "Maurice Prendergast, 1859–1924," catalogue, Boston Museum of Fine Arts, October–December 1960, text by Hedley H. Rhys; *Maurice Prendergast Water-Color Sketchbook 1899.* Harvard University Press, Cambridge, 1960, critical note by Peter A. Wick; Cambell, Lawrence. "Prendergast," *Portfolio and Art News Annual*, no. 4, 1961, pp. 128–137, 149–156; "Paintings and Water Colors by Maurice Prendergast," catalogue, Knoedler Galleries, New York, November 1966, essay by Charles H. Sawyer.

139 *Summer Afternoon.* c. 1909.
Water color and pastel, 13 × 19⅛ in. (33 × 48.5 cm.).
Signed lower left "Prendergast."

140 *Summer Day.* n.d.
Water color and pastel, 13 × 18¾ in. (33 × 47.8 cm.).
Signed three times, lower left, center and lower right "Prendergast—Prendergast—Prendergast."

141 *Play Time.* n.d.
Water color and pastel, 14⅜ × 21⅝ in. (36.5 × 55 cm.).

142 *Outskirts of Village.* n.d. *
Water color and pastel, 13¼ × 19¼ in. (33.6 × 49 cm.).
Signed lower center "Prendergast."

EXHIBITIONS: Dayton Art Institute, Dayton, Ohio. "Maurice Prendergast, Paintings," February 1948; Philbrook Art Center, Tulsa, 1956; Museum of Fine Arts, St. Petersburg 1968.

143 *Massachusetts Shore.* n.d.
Water color and pastel, 13½ × 19½ in. (34.1 × 49.5 cm.).
Signed lower left "Prendergast."

144 *South Side Hills.* n.d. *
Water color, 13 × 18⅞ in. (33 × 47.9 cm.).
Signed lower left "Prendergast."

EXHIBITIONS: Dayton Art Institute, Dayton, Ohio, "Maurice Prendergast, Paintings," February 1948.

149 Mâurice Brazil Prendergast *Along the Shore* c. 1917

145 Maurice Brazil Prendergast *St. Malo No.* 1 c. 1910

147 Maurice Brazil Prendergast *Venice* n.d.

148 Maurice Brazil Prendergast *The Promenade* c. 1913 (?)

151 Maurice Brazil Prendergast *Resting, St. Malo* c. 1919

145 *St. Malo, No. 1.* c. 1910. *
Water color, 13⅝ × 19⅜ in. (34.3 × 49.3 cm.).
Signed lower left "Prendergast."

Prendergast remained a solitary and original figure, even while informally associated with *The Eight*. In the *St. Malo* studies, he subordinated figurative details, concentrating instead on nuances of light, air and color. The expanded and finely tuned sense Of space in these water colors recalls Cézanne's spatial concerns, which Prendergast absorbed and rendered indigenous to his own vision.

EXHIBITIONS: John Herron Art Institute, Indianapolis, Indiana, "Water Colors by American Artists," 1 February–8 March 1944; Indiana University, Bloomington, Indiana, 10–25 March 1944; Dayton Art Institute, Dayton, Ohio, "Maurice Prendergast, Paintings," February 1948; Norton Gallery of Art, West Palm Beach, Florida, "Masters of Water Colors—Marin, Demuth and Prendergast," 3–26 February 1950, no. 28; Carnegie Institute, 1952; Philbrook Art Center, 1956; Albany Institute, 1958; American Federation of Arts, New York, "Adventures in Collecting," October 1958–October 1960; Allentown Art Museum, Allentown, Pennsylvania, 1–18 April 1961.

146 *St. Malo, No. 2.* c. 1910.
Water color, 12⅞ × 19⅜ in. (32.8 × 49 cm.).
Signed lower center "Prendergast."

147 *Venice.* n.d. *
Water color, 14¾ × 21½ in. (37.5 × 54.5 cm.).
Signed lower right "Prendergast."

During Prendergast's first visit to Europe in 1898–1899, he allied himself with the Nabis and the Symbolists, adapting their brilliant hues to his own impressionist style. A trip to Italy, especially to Venice, which he visited again in 1912, intensified the vivid palette that characterizes his work. In this study, the spontaneity of the water color medium enabled him to move away from illustration and to capture the flowing quality of light and movement to which he was attracted.

EXHIBITIONS: Cincinnati Art Museum, 1935; John Herron Art Institute, Indianapolis, Indiana, "Water Colors by American Artists," 1 February–8 March 1944; Indiana University, Bloomington, Indiana, 10–25 March 1944; Dayton Art Institute, Dayton, Ohio, "Maurice Prendergast, Paintings," February 1948; Norton Gallery of Art, West Palm Beach, Florida, "Masters of Water Colors—Marin, Demuth and Prendergast," 3–26 February 1950, no. 25; Philbrook Art Center, 1956; Albany Institute, 1958; American Federation Of Arts, New York, "Adventures in Collecting," October 1958–October 1960; Allentown Art Museum, Allentown, Pennsylvania, 1–18 April 1961.

148 *The Promenade.* c. 1913 (?). *
Oil on canvas, 28 × 40⅛ in. (71 × 101.7 cm.).
Signed lower left "Prendergast."

EXHIBITIONS: Horace Rackham School of Graduate Studies, University of Michigan, Ann Arbor, Michigan, "American Painting," 1–31 July 1940, no. 34; Dayton Art Institute, Dayton, Ohio, "Maurice Prendergast, Paintings," February 1948; Dayton Art Institute, Dayton, Ohio, "America and Impressionism," 19 October–11 November 1951; Marquette University, Milwaukee, Wisconsin, "Festival of American Arts," 20 April–20 May 1956; American Federation of Arts, New York, "Children of the City," circulating exhibition, January 1957–June 1958.

REPRODUCED: *The Arts*, vol. 8, August 1925, p. 70.

149 *Along the Shore.* c. 1917. *
Oil on canvas, 23⅛ × 34⅛ in. (58.7 × 86.6 cm.).
Signed lower left "Prendergast."

Although absorbed with the expression of contemporary pageantry, Prendergast never denied his close ties with the art-historical past. Especially taken with Carpaccio's stately 16th century Venetian views, he captured the vivacity of his own era while retaining the grandeur and brilliance evoked by the earlier master.

EXHIBITIONS: Whitney Museum, New York, "Maurice Prendergast Memorial Exhibition," 21 February–22 March 1934, no. 66; Cincinnati Art Museum, 1935; Dayton Art Institute, Dayton, Ohio, "Maurice Prendergast, Paintings," February 1948; Birmingham Museum of Art, Birmingham, Alabama, "Opening Exhibition," 8 April–3 June 1951, p. 49; Carnegie Institute, 1952; American Federation of Arts, New York, "Children of the City," circulating exhibition January 1957–June 1958; Indiana University Museum of Art, Bloomington, Indiana, "American Painting 1910–1960," 19 April–10 May 1964, no. 55, illus.

150 *Outer Harbor.* n.d. *
Oil on panel, 18½ × 32¼ in. (47 × 81.6 cm.).

In later years Prendergast renewed his earlier interest in individual characterization (see, for example, no. 152); however, he remains best-known for the densely packed, jewelled mosaic style found in this painting.

Born the same year as the pointillist Seurat, Prendergast also used dabs of unmixed color. However, he emphasized the prismatic juxtaposition of hues rather than their optical blend.

In terms of formal organization and poetic impact, such paintings are entirely contemporary, and have led to the recent re-evaluation of Prendergast as a pioneer Modernist in this century.

EXHIBITIONS: Dayton Art Institute, Dayton, Ohio, "Maurice Prendergast, Paintings," February 1948; Dayton Art Institute, Dayton, Ohio, "America & Impressionism," 19 October–11 November 1951; Norfolk Museum, Norfolk, Virginia, "Significant American Moderns," March–April 1953; Contemporary Arts Center of Cincinnati Art Museum and Dayton Art Institute, Ohio, "An American Viewpoint: Realism in Twentieth Century Painting," 10 October 1957–15 January 1958; Otterbein College, Westerville, Ohio, March 1965.

151 *Resting, St. Malo*. c. 1919. *
Oil on canvas, 24 × 30 in. (60.7 × 76.1 cm.).
Signed lower right "Prendergast."

EXHIBITIONS: Museum of Living Art, New York University, New York, "Opening Exhibition," 13 December 1927–25 January 1928; Art Institute of Chicago, Chicago, Illinois, "A Century of Progress, Exhibition of Paintings and Sculpture," 1 June–1 November 1933, no. 470; Whitney Museum, New York, "Maurice Prendergast Memorial Exhibition," 21 February–22 March 1934, no. 111; Dayton Art Institute, Dayton, Ohio, "Maurice Prendergast, Paintings," February 1948; Allen Memorial Art Museum, Oberlin, Ohio, 20 November 1950–10 September 1951; University of Iowa, Iowa City, Iowa, "Summer Festival, Modern American Painting," 25 May–2 August 1962; Denison University, Granville, Ohio, 15 September–15 November 1962; Museum of Fine Arts, St. Petersburg, 1968.

152 *Children*. c. 1919–1920.
Water color and pastel, 11⅜ × 9⅝ in. (28.8 × 24.5 cm.).
Signed lower right "Prendergast."

Theodore Robinson (1852–1896)

Born Irasburg, Vermont, 1852. Moved to Evansville, Wisconsin, in 1856. Went to Chicago in 1869 or 1870 to study art, but his chronic asthma forced him to return home. Studied in New York at National Academy of Design in 1874. Left for Paris in 1876, where he studied with Gerôme and Carolus-Duran. Works shown in Paris Salon in 1877 and 1879. Exhibited in New York at the Society of American Artists in 1878 and annually thereafter. Returned to New York in 1879. Spent next fifteen years living in Paris, Southern France and New York City. Taught private art classes in New York where he also assisted John La Farge in 1881, and later Prentice Treadwell, with mural commissions. Began exhibiting at the National Academy in 1881. Started painting from photographs in early 1880's. Became friends with Monet in 1888 and wrote an article about him for *Century Magazine* in 1892. Was close friends with J. Alden Weir and John Twachtman. Works shown jointly with Theodore Wendel's in Boston in 1892. Taught summer classes for the Brooklyn Art School in 1893 and 1894. Taught at Pennsylvania Academy of Fine Arts in 1895. First one-man show held at Macbeth Gallery in New York that year. Died in New York in 1896.

BIBLIOGRAPHY: Robinson, Theodore, essays on Monet, Van Dyke and Corot in *Modern French Masters*, 1896; Clark, E. "Theodore Robinson," *Art in America*, vol. VI, 1917–1918, pp. 286–294; Clark, E. "Theodore Robinson, A Pioneer American Impressionist," *Scribner's Magazine* (London), vol. 70, 1921, pp. 763–768; Cortissoz, Royal. *American Artists*. New York 1923; "Theodore Robinson, 1852–1896," catalogue, Brooklyn Museum, 12 November 1946–5 January 1947, text by John I. H. Baur; Lewison, Florence. "Theodore Robinson, America's First Impressionist," *American Artist*, vol. 27, no. 2, February 1963, pp. 40–45.

153 *Fifth Avenue at Twenty-Third Street*. 1895.
Oil on canvas, 24⅛ × 19⅛ in. (61.3 × 48.6 cm.).
Signed lower left "Th. Robinson."

In 1894, Robinson was commissioned by Jaccaci, art editor at Scribner's, to do a view of Fifth Avenue. As with many of his figure compositions, he worked from photographs, attempting to reconcile realism with his profound interest in Impressionist ideas. This dualism stems, in part, from his studies abroad with such academicians as Gérôme and Carolus-Duran; their influence was countered by Robinson's close friendship with Monet, whom he nevertheless criticized as having "complete disrespect for form." The dichotomy between academic and radical interests, typical of American art at the turn of the century, was never resolved by Robinson, but his fresh, candid eye and sensitive draughtsmanship produced many delightful vignettes of the period.

EXHIBITIONS: Brooklyn Museum, Brooklyn, New York, "Theodore Robinson, 1852–1896," 12 November 1946–5 January 1947, no. 66; Dayton Art Institute, Dayton, Ohio, "America and Impressionism," 19 October–11 November 1951; University of Wisconsin, Madison, Wisconsin, "Theodore Robinson, An American Impressionist," 29 October–10 November 1964, no. 20, illus.

REPRODUCED: Watson, Forbes. "American Collections, Number one—The Ferdinand Howald Collection," *Arts*, vol. 8, August 1925, p. 64.

150 Maurice Brazil Prendergast *Outer Harbor* n.d.

153 Theodore Robinson *Fifth Avenue at Twenty-Third Street* 1895

Morton Schamberg (1881–1918)

Born Philadelphia, 1881. Attended University of Pennsylvania from 1899 to 1903, graduating with a Bachelor's degree in architecture. Studied at the Pennsylvania Academy of Fine Arts from 1903 until 1906 with William Merritt Chase. Spent summers of 1902 in Holland, 1903 in England and 1904 in Spain with Chase's summer classes. Met Charles Sheeler while both were students at the Academy. They became close friends, sharing a studio in Philadelphia from 1906 to 1909. Went to Paris in 1906 for a year, then returned to Philadelphia. Travelled to Europe again in 1908, joining Sheeler in Italy and going with him to Paris for a few months in 1909. Back in Philadelphia around 1910, he and Sheeler rented a house in Doylestown, Pennsylvania, where they sketched on the weekends. Had one-man show at McClees Gallery, Philadelphia, in 1910. Around 1913, he turned to photography to supplement his income from painting. Stieglitz later encouraged him in photography. Invited by Arthur B. Davies in 1912 to participate in Armory Show of 1913, where five of his works subsequently appeared. Also exhibited in group show at Montross Gallery, New York, 1913. Assembled an exhibition for McClees Gallery in 1915 of several artists' works that had appeared in the Armory Show. It caused a furor in Philadelphia and alienated Shamberg's friend and teacher, William Merritt Chase. Met Duchamp at home of Walter Arensberg in New York City, and in 1916 was among the first artists to use machines as subject matter in his paintings. Died suddenly in flu epidemic in Philadelphia in 1918.

BIBLIOGRAPHY: McAgy, Douglas. "5 Rediscovered from the Last Generation," *Art News*, vol. 59, no. 4, Summer 1960, pp. 38–41; Wolf, Ben. *Morton Livingston Schamberg*. Philadelphia 1963, includes 1913, statement by Schamberg reviews of 1919 Schamberg exhibition by Walter Pach and Henry McBride; Wolf, Ben. "Morton Livingston Schamberg," *Art in America*, vol. 52, no. 1, February 1963, pp. 76–86.

154 *Composition*. 1916. *
Water color, 11½ × 9½ in. (29.2 × 24.1 cm.).
Signed upper right "Schamberg."

EXHIBITIONS: Allentown Art Museum, Allentown, Pennsylvania, 1–18 April 1961; Pennsylvania Academy of Fine Arts, Philadelphia, "The Works of Morton L. Schamberg, Retrospective Exhibition," 21 November–24 December 1963, no. 24; Zabriskie Gallery, New York, "Morton L. Schamberg Exhibition," 6–26 January 1964, no. 10.

REPRODUCED: Wolf, Ben. *Morton Livingston Schamberg*. University of Pennsylvania Press, Philadelphia, 1963, p. 97.

155 *Telephone*. 1916. *
Oil on canvas, 24 × 20 in. (61 × 50.9 cm.).
Signed and dated upper right "Schamberg 1916."

Schamberg was an innovator and a harbinger, in the United States, of the mechanistic idiom utilized by the Dadaists Picabia and Duchamp. Unlike his American contemporaries (with the exception of Sheeler, who was a close friend) he drew his inspiration uniquely from the precise, matter-of-fact forms of the machine.

In this painting, Schamberg utilizes geometric, frontal planes in order to make a distinction between "the mere representation or rendering of space and designing in space." To this end, he has employed a continuing shift of emphasis between light and dark values, rounded and rectilinear shapes, linear and modeled forms.

EXHIBITIONS: Walker Art Center, 1960; University of Iowa, Iowa City, Iowa, "Summer Festival, Modern American Painting," 25 May–2 August 1962; Pennsylvania Academy of Fine Arts, Philadelphia, "The Works of Morton L. Schamberg, Retrospective Exhibition," 21 November–24 December 1963, no. 32; Zabriskie Gallery, New York, "Morton L. Schamberg Exhibition," 6–26 January 1964, no. 17, illus.; Smithsonian Institution, Washington, D.C., "Roots of Abstract Art in America 1910–1930," 1 December 1965–16 January 1966, no. 146, illus.; University of New Mexico Art Museum, 1967.

REPRODUCED: Brown, Milton. *American Painting from the Armory Show to the Depression*. Princeton 1955, p. 117; Pierson, William H., Jr. and Davidson, Martha. (eds.). *Arts of the U.S., A Pictorial Survey*. New York 1960, p. 358, no. 3353; *Arts*, vol. 38, no. 6, March 1964, p. 61; Wolf, Ben. *Morton Livingston Schamberg*. University of Pennsylvania Press, Philadelphia, 1963, pl. 98; Milwaukee Art Center, Milwaukee, Wisconsin, "Pop Art and the American Tradition," 9 April–9 May 1965.

Saul Schary (1904–)

Born Newark, New Jersey, 1904. Studied at Fawcett Art School in Newark and in evening classes at Art Students League. Also attended Philadelphia Academy of Fine Arts. Studied in Paris at La Grande Chaumière; returned to New York in 1927. Had first one-man show at Daniel Gallery around 1930, from which Ferdinand Howald bought a water color. Works appeared in Whitney Museum of American Art annual exhibitions in 1941, 1942 and 1943. Lives in New York City.

156 *Abstraction, New York*. 1929.
Water color, 13 × 10⅜ in. (33 × 26.4 cm.).
Signed lower right "Schary."

Alice Schille (1869–1955)

157 *Midsummer Day*. n.d.
Water color, 11½ × 13½ in. (29.2 × 34.3 cm.).
Signed lower right "A. Schille."

158 *Sea and Tidal River*. n.d.
Water color, 11½ × 13⅝ in. (29.2 × 34.6 cm.).
Signed lower right "A. Schille."

Charles Sheeler (1883–1965)

Born Philadelphia, 1883. Studied applied design at Philadelphia School of Industrial Art, 1900 to 1903. Attended Pennsylvania Academy of Fine Arts where he studied with William Merritt Chase. Accompanied Chase on summer study trips to England and Holland in 1904 and to Spain in 1905. Opened studio in Philadelphia in 1906 with Morton Schamberg, a close friend and former Academy classmate. Painting shown in winter exhibition, National Academy of Design, New York, in 1906; exhibited there in 1907 and 1908. Works shown at Academy of Fine Arts, Philadelphia, in 1907 and annually until 1919. Had first one-man show at McClees Gallery, Philadelphia, in 1908. Travelled in Italy in 1908; met Schamberg there and went to Paris with him in early 1909, where Sheeler's traditional aesthetic was jolted by works of Cézanne and the Cubists. Returned to Philadelphia in 1909. Rented house in Doylestown, Pennsylvania in 1910 where he and Schamberg sketched. Began photographing architecture in 1912 to supplement income from painting. Six works shown in Armory Show, 1913. Visited New York City frequently where he met Marius De Zayas and Walter Arensberg. Works appeared in group shows at Montross Gallery, New York in 1915, 1916, 1917 and 1923, and in the "Forum Exhibition," Anderson Galleries, New York, in 1916. Exhibited photographs taken in Doylestown at De Zayas' Modern Gallery, New York, in 1917; paintings shown in Society of Independent Artists first annual exhibition that year. Moved to New York after Schamberg's death in 1918. Photographs won top prizes at Wanamaker's annual exhibition, New York, in 1918. After photographing De Zayas' collection of primitive art, he received several commissions to photograph other private collections. Worked in De Zayas' gallery from 1920 until 1923; had one-man show of paintings and photographs there in 1920. Collaborated with Paul Strand on film study of New York City architecture titled "Manhatta" in 1921. One-man show of paintings held at Daniel Gallery, New York, 1922. Worked as commercial photographer for the publisher Condé Nast from 1923 until around 1931. Wrote articles for *The Arts* magazine on Stieglitz' photography in May 1923 and on ancient Greek art in March 1925. Assembled show of works by Picasso, Braque, Duchamp and others for the Whitney Studio Club in 1926; his own works were shown there concurrently. Moved to South Salem, New York, in 1927. Did photographic essay of Ford Motor Company's River Rouge plant in Michigan in 1927. Took last trip abroad in 1929, travelling to France where he photographed Chartres Cathedral and to Germany where his photographs were in "Film und Foto" exhibition in Stuttgart. Downtown Gallery, New York, became his dealer in 1931. Had one-man show at Arts Club of Chicago in 1932. Moved to Ridgefield, Connecticut, in 1933. Took photographic studies of colonial Williamsburg, Virginia, in 1935. Retrospective of works at Museum of Modern Art, New York, in 1939. Worked on commission as painter and photographer for *Fortune* magazine in 1939 and 1940. Resulting six paintings on theme "Power" were shown at Downtown Gallery in 1940. Worked as photographer for Metropolitan Museum of Art, New York, from 1942 until 1945. Was artist in residence at Phillips Academy, Andover, Massachusetts, in 1946 and at the Currier Gallery, Manchester, New Hampshire, in 1948. Retrospective exhibition held at University of California Art Galleries, Los Angeles, in 1954. Incapacitated by a stroke in 1959. Died in 1965.

BIBLIOGRAPHY: Rourke, Constance M. *Charles Sheeler, Artist in the American Tradition*. New York, 1938; "Charles Sheeler, Paintings, Drawings, Photographs," catalogue, Museum of Modern Art, 1939, introduction by William Carlos Williams; "Charles Sheeler, A Retrospective Exhibition," catalogue, University of California, Los Angeles, 1954, essays by Bartlett Hayes, Jr., Frederick S. Wight; Richardson, E. P. "Three American Painters," *Perspectives, U.S.A.*, no. 16, Summer 1956, pp. 111–119; Cohen, George Michael. "Charles Sheeler," *American Artist*, vol. 23, no. 1, January 1959, pp. 32–37, 66–68; "The Quest of Charles Sheeler," catalogue, University of Iowa, March–April 1963, essay by Lillian Dochterman; Tillim, Sidney. "Dissent on the Armory Show," *Arts*, vol. 37, no. 8–9, May–June 1963, pp. 96–101; Andrews, Faith and Edward D. "Sheeler and the Shakers," *Art in America*, vol. 53, no. 1, February 1965, pp. 90–95; "Charles Sheeler," catalogue, National Collection of Fine Arts, Smithsonian Institution, October–November 1968, essays by Martin Friedman, Bartlett Hayes, Charles Millard; Kramer, Hilton. "Charles Sheeler, American Pastoral," *Artforum*, vol. VII, no. 5, January 1969, pp. 36–39.

159 *Lhasa*. 1916. *
(Original title *Impressionism* changed by Sheeler in 1939).
Oil on canvas, 25½ × 31¾ in. (65 × 80 cm.).
Signed and dated lower right "Sheeler 1916."

In 1939, on the occasion of a retrospective exhibition of his work at the Museum of Modern Art, New York, Sheeler commented on his earlier works. Of the pictures done during the second decade, he wrote:

"(This is a period) when a consciousness of structure and design as essential considerations was first becoming evident in my work. While the use of

154 Morton Schamberg *Composition* 1916

155 Morton Schamberg *Telephone* 1916

159 Charles Sheeler *Lhasa* 1916

160 Charles Sheeler *Bucks County Barn* 1918

163 Charles Sheeler *Still Life* 1921

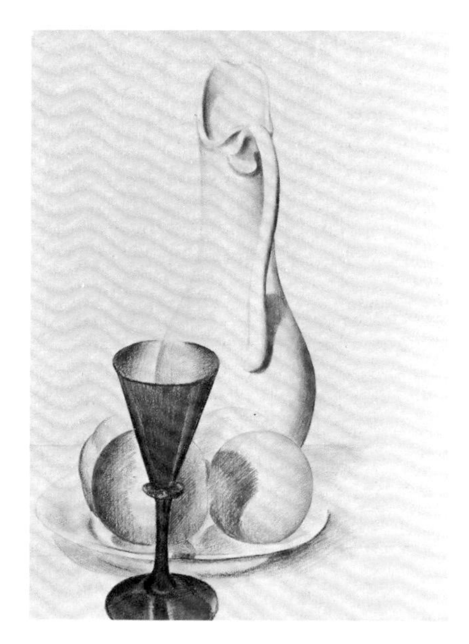

165 Charles Sheeler
Still Life with Peaches 1923

natural forms has for the most part been prevalent in my painting, a brief excursion into abstraction was made. These abstract studies were invariably derived directly from forms seen in nature, *Flower Forms* and *Lhasa* being offered in evidence. The duration of this period was determined by the growing belief that pictures realistically conceived might have an underlying abstract structure. This belief has continued with me as a working principle . . ."

EXHIBITIONS: Museum of Modern Art, New York, "Charles Sheeler: Paintings, Drawings, Photographs," 4 October–1 November 1939, no. 8; Dayton Art Institute, Dayton, Ohio, "Paintings by Charles Sheeler," 1–30 November 1944; Whitney Museum, New York, "Pioneers of Modern Art in America," 9 April–12 May 1946, circulated by American Federation of Arts 1946–1947, no. 139, illus.; Cincinnati Art Museum, Cincinnati, Ohio, "Paintings: From 1900–1925," 2 February–4 March 1951, no. 58 (titled *Impressionism*); Carnegie Institute, 1952; Art Galleries, University of California, Los Angeles, California, "Charles Sheeler: Retrospective Exhibition," October 1954, and tour to M. H. De Young Memorial Museum, San Francisco, Fort Worth Art Center, Munson-Williams-Proctor Institute, Utica, New York, San Diego Fine Arts Gallery, no. 2; American Federation of Arts, New York, "Pioneers of American Abstract Art," circulating exhibition, December 1955–January 1957, no. 40; Allentown Art Museum, Allentown, Pennsylvania, "Charles Sheeler: Retrospective Exhibition," 17 November–31 December 1961, no. 3; Downtown Gallery, New York, "Abstract Painting in America 1903–1923," 27 March–21 April 1962; University of Iowa, Iowa City, Iowa, "Summer Festival, Modern American Painting," 25 May–2 August 1962; Denison University, Granville, Ohio, "Modern American Painting," 15 September–15 November 1962; Corcoran Gallery, Washington, D.C. "The New Tradition," 27 April–2 June 1963, no. 89; Poses Institute of Fine Arts, Brandeis University, Waltham, Massachusetts, "Modernism: The First Wave, Paintings from 1903–1933," 4 October–10 November 1963, illus.; Smithsonian Institution, Washington, D.C. "Roots of Abstract Art in America 1910–1930," 1 December 1965–16 January 1966, no. 151, illus.; ACA American Heritage Gallery, New York, "50th Anniversary of the Forum Exhibition of Modern Painters, March 1916," 14 March–9 April 1966, no. 34, illus.; University of New Mexico Art Museum, 1967, illus. p. 52; Museum of Fine Arts, St. Petersburg, 1968; National Collection of Fine Arts, Smithsonian Institution, Washington, D.C. "Charles Sheeler," 10 October–24 November 1968, and tour to Philadelphia Museum of Art, January–February 1969, Whitney Museum, March–April 1969, no. 13, illus. p. 71.

160 *Bucks County Barn*. 1918. *
Water color and gouache, 17 × 22½ in. (43 × 57 cm.).
Signed and dated lower right "Sheeler 1918."

Sheeler's directness, his desire to render with clarity and precision the artifacts of the Machine Age, and above all his rigorous adaptation of cubist vocabulary to architectural phenomena characterize the Cubist-Realist pictures he painted until the late 1920's.

Sheeler's profound interest in realism links his remarkable talents as a photographer with the extraordinary draughtsmanship of his paintings.

In *Bucks County Barn*, flat planes are isolated against a clear field, forcing focus on textural and volumetric juxtapositions. Sheeler refused to romanticize or distort the actual visual data he dealt with. Consequently, these naked, dehumanized "landscapes" (barns, factories, cities, interiors) may be seen as a pictorial phenomenology, an attempt to grasp the essence of the thing viewed by treating it in terms of its physical manifestation rather than its symbolic overtones.

EXHIBITIONS: De Zayas Gallery, New York, "Exhibition of Work of Charles Sheeler," 16–23 February 1920; Pennsylvania Academy of Fine Arts, Philadelphia, Pennsylvania, "Tendencies in Art," 1921; Cincinnati Art Museum, 1935; Cincinnati Modern Art Society, Cincinnati, Ohio, "A New Realism," 12 March–7 April 1941, no. 14; Dayton Art Institute, Dayton, Ohio, "Paintings by Charles Sheeler," 1–30 November 1944; American Federation of Arts, New York, "Early 20th Century American Watercolors," circulating exhibition, 1 August 1948–1 June 1949; Carnegie Institute, 1952; Worcester Art Museum, Worcester, Massachusetts, "Five Painters of America: Bouché, Hopper, Shahn, Sheeler, Wyeth," 17 February–3 April 1955; Albany Institute, 1958; American Federation of Arts, New York, "Adventures in Collecting," October 1958–October 1960, no. 38; University of Iowa, Iowa City, Iowa, "The Quest of Charles Sheeler," 17 March–14 April 1963, no. 14, illus. no. 5; ACA American Heritage Gallery, New York, "50th Anniversary of the Forum Exhibition of Modern American Painters, March 1916," 14 March–9 April 1966; Museum of Fine Arts, St. Petersburg, 1968; National Collection of Fine Arts, Smithsonian Institution, Washington, D.C., "Charles Sheeler," 10 October–24 November 1968, and tour to Philadelphia Museum of Art, January–February 1969, Whitney Museum, March–April 1969.

REPRODUCED: Kramer, Hilton. "Charles Sheeler: American Pastoral," *Artforum*, vol. VII, no. 5, January 1969, p. 39.

161 *Flower in Bowl*. 1918.
Water color and gouache, 14⅝ × 11⅝ in. (41.1 × 29.5 cm.).
Signed and dated lower right "Sheeler 1918."

162 *Zinnias*. 1918.
Water color and gouache, 13½ × 9⅛ in. (34.5 × 23.1 cm.).
Signed and dated lower right "Sheeler 1918."

163 *Still Life*. 1921. *
Pencil, 13 × 15 1/16 in. (33.1 × 38.3 cm.).
Signed and dated lower right "Sheeler 1921."

EXHIBITIONS: Museum of Modern Art, New York, "Charles Sheeler: Paintings, Drawings, Photographs," 4 October–1 November 1939, no. 53; Dayton Art Institute, Dayton, Ohio, "Drawings by Contemporary Moderns," 1–30 September 1943; Dayton Art Institute, Dayton, Ohio, "Paintings by Charles Sheeler," 1–30 November 1944; University of Iowa, Iowa City, Iowa, "The Quest of Charles Sheeler," 17 March–14 April 1963, no. 17, illus. no. 8; Museum of Fine Arts, St. Petersburg, 1968.

164 *Dahlias and White Pitcher*. 1923. *
Water color, 26 × 19½ in. (65.8 × 49.5 cm.).
Signed and dated lower right "Sheeler 1923."

Sheeler's still-lifes, although less formal than his architectonic vistas, remained objective and concise. In this flower study, crisp, controlled contours and shadows are offset by the flat background plane. Objects are intensified and subjected to a minute delineation of volume and surface.

EXHIBITIONS: Cincinnati Art Museum, 1935; Museum of Modern Art, New York, "Charles Sheeler, Paintings, Drawings, Photographs," 4 October–1 November 1939, no. 56; University of Michigan, Ann Arbor, Michigan, "Exhibition of American Painting," 1–31 July 1940, no. 41, illus. p. 15; Dayton Art Institute, Dayton, Ohio, "Paintings by Charles Sheeler," 1–30 November 1944; Norfolk Museum, Norfolk, Virginia, "Charles Sheeler Retrospective Exhibition," February–April 1953; Albany Institute, 1958; American Federation of Arts, New York, "Adventures in Collecting," October 1958–October 1960, no. 41; Allentown Art Museum, Allentown, Pennsylvania, "Charles Sheeler: Retrospective Exhibition," 17 November–31 December 1961, no. 5; University of Iowa, Iowa City, Iowa, "The Quest of Charles Sheeler," 17 March–14 April 1963, no. 21; Museum of Fine Arts, St. Petersburg, 1968.

REPRODUCED: *International Studio*, vol. LXXXIV, no. 348, May 1926, p. 68. Rourke, Constance. *Charles Sheeler, Artist in the American Tradition*. New York, 1938, p. 64 (titled *Chrysanthemums*).

165 *Still Life with Peaches*. 1923. *
Pastel, 15¾ × 11½ in. (40 × 29 cm.).
Signed and dated lower right "Sheeler 1923."

EXHIBITIONS: Museum of Modern Art, New York, "Charles Sheeler: Paintings, Drawings, Photographs," 4 October–1 November 1939, no. 57, illus.; Dayton Art Institute, Dayton, Ohio, "Paintings by Charles Sheeler," 1–30 November 1944; American Federation of Arts, New York, "Early 20th Century American Water Colors," circulating exhibition, 1 August 1948–1 June 1949; Worcester Art Museum, Worcester, Massachusetts, "Five Painters of America: Bouché, Hopper, Shahn, Sheeler, Wyeth," 17 February–3 April 1955; Philbrook Art Center, 1956; University of Iowa, Iowa City, Iowa, "The Quest of Charles Sheeler," 17 March–14 April 1963; Museum of Fine Arts, St. Petersburg, 1968; National Collection of Fine Arts, Smithsonian Institution, Washington, D.C., "Charles Sheeler," 10 October–24 November 1968, and tour to Philadelphia Museum of Art, January–February 1969, Whitney Museum, March–April 1969, no. 30, illus. p. 63.

166 *Objects on a Table*. (*Still Life with White Teapot*.) 1924. *
Black conte crayon and tempera, 31 × 21 in. (78.5 × 53.3 cm.).
Signed and dated lower right "Sheeler 1924."

The rigorously austere, vertical and simplified composition of this still life is a perfect expression of Sheeler's attitude toward the objects he portrayed. His interest in domestic interiors, especially those of the Shakers, led him to an ever more geometric, unpretentious rendering of the commonplace.

The pale, cold light which bathes his pictures flattens forms and gives equal weight to tangible and intangible shapes; thus, the shadows cast by table, glass and pitcher appear as corporeal as the objects themselves.

EXHIBITIONS: Cincinnati Art Museum, 1935; Museum of Modern Art, New York, "Charles Sheeler: Paintings, Drawings, Photographs," 4 October–1 November 1939, no. 65, illus. p. 20 (titled *Still Life with White Teapot*); Dayton Institute of Art, Dayton, Ohio, "Paintings by Charles Sheeler," 1–30 November 1944; American Federation of Arts, New York, "Early 20th Century American Water Colors," circulating exhibition, 1 August 1948–1 June 1949; Carnegie Institute, 1952; Art Galleries, University of California, Los Angeles, California, "Charles Sheeler: Retrospective Exhibition," October 1954, and tour to M. H. De Young Memorial Museum, San Francisco, Fort Worth Art Center, Munson-Williams-Proctor Institute, Utica, New York, San Diego Fine Arts Gallery, no. 8; Philbrook Art Center, 1956; Albany Institute, 1958; American Federation of Arts, New York, "Adventures in Collecting," October 1958–October 1960; Allentown Art Museum, Allentown, Pennsylvania, 1–18 April 1961; University of Iowa, Iowa City,

164 Charles Sheeler *Dahlias and White Pitcher* 1923

166 Charles Sheeler *Objects on a Table* (*Still Life with White Teapot*) 1924

Iowa, "The Quest of Charles Sheeler," 17 March–14 April 1963, no. 26, illus. no. 9; Flint Institute of Arts, Flint, Michigan, "Realism Revisited," 27 April–30 May 1966, illus. p. 4; Cedar Rapids Art Center, Cedar Rapids, Iowa, "Charles Sheeler: A Retrospective Exhibition," 25 October–26 November 1967; Museum of Fine Arts, St. Petersburg, 1968; National Collection of Fine Arts, Smithsonian Institution, Washington, D.C. "Charles Sheeler," 10 October–24 November 1968, and tour to Philadelphia Museum of Art January–February 1969, Whitney Museum, March–April 1969, no. 33, illus. p. 115.

REPRODUCED: Rourke, Constance. *Charles Sheeler, Artist in the American Tradition*. New York 1938. p. 73 (titled *Still Life with White Teapot*); Born, Wolfgang. *Still-life Painting in America*. Oxford, 1947, pl. 131 (titled *Still Life with Teapot*); Kramer, Hilton. "Charles Sheeler: American Pastoral," *Artforum*, vol. VII, no. 5, January 1969, p. 39.

Raphael Soyer (1899–)

Born Tambov, Russia, in 1899. Brothers Moses and Isaac also became artists. Came to U.S. in 1912, settled in New York. Studied evenings at Cooper Union, then attended classes at the National Academy around 1919. Studied at the Art Students League in the mid-1920's under Guy Pène DuBois. Painting shown at "Salons of America" exhibition in 1926 seen by Alexander Brook who then helped Soyer sell his work at the Whitney Studio Club and the Daniel Gallery. Had first one-man show at Daniel Gallery in 1929, from which Ferdinand Howald bought a painting. Went abroad in 1935, travelling in Western Europe and the U.S.S.R. Portraits exhibited at ACA Gallery, New York, 1965. One-man show held at Forum Gallery, New York, 1966. Retrospective Exhibition at the Whitney Museum of American Art in 1967. Has taught at Art Students League, American Artists School, New School for Social Research and National Academy of Design.

BIBLIOGRAPHY: *Raphael Soyer*. American Artists Group, New York, 1946; Soyer, Raphael. *A Painter's Pilgrimage*. New York 1962; Soyer, Raphael. *Homage to Thomas Eakins, Etc.* South Brunswick, 1966; "Raphael Soyer," catalogue, Whitney Museum, 1967, introduction by Lloyd Goodrich; Gutman, Walter, Jerome Klein and Raphael Soyer. *Raphael Soyer, Paintings and Drawings*. New York, 1960.

167 *Odalisque*. 1924–1928. *
Oil on canvas, 25⅛ × 20⅛ in. (63.9 × 51 cm.).
Signed and dated lower right "Raphael Soyer 1924–28."

EXHIBITIONS: Daniel Gallery, New York, 1929; Cincinnati Art Museum, 1935; Dayton Art Institute, 1941.

REPRODUCED: *Creative Art*, April 1930, p. 258; Gutman, Klein. *Raphael Soyer*. New York 1960, p. 48.

Niles Spencer (1893–1952)

Born Pawtucket, Rhode Island, 1893. Studied at Rhode Island School of Design from 1913 to 1915. Painted with Charles Woodbury at Ogunquit, Maine, during summers of 1914 and 1915. Became evening instructor at Rhode Island School of Design in 1915. But his teaching was influenced by study with Henri and Bellows in New York and he was soon dismissed from his position for "progressiveness." Moved to New York City in 1916 to take more courses with Henri and Bellows at the Art Students League. Knew Bouché, Kuniyoshi and Hartley; became close friends with Demuth and Sheeler after 1922. Moved to Ogunquit in 1917. Went to Paris in 1921 where he saw works by cubists and Cézanne; also travelled in Italy. Returned to the U.S. and New York in 1923. Joined the Whitney Studio Club that year, exhibiting there until 1930. Had one-man shows at Daniel Gallery, New York, in 1925 and 1928. Lived in New York City and Dingman's Ferry, Pennsylvania, until 1923 when he opened a summer studio in Provincetown, Massachusetts. Painted in Bermuda in 1927–1928. Took second trip to France in 1928; painted in Paris and Villefranche-sur-mer on the Riviera. Works shown in "Painting and Sculpture by Living Americans" at Museum of Modern Art, New York, 1930. Experience painting a mural in Pennsylvania steel town of Aliquippa, 1937, strengthened his preference for industrial subject matter. Exhibited works in "New Realism" show at Cincinnati Modern Art Society in 1941. Painted in Dingman's Ferry, Sag Harbor, Long Island, and New York from 1947 until 1952. One-man show held at Downtown Gallery in 1947. Died in Dingman's Ferry in 1952.

BIBLIOGRAPHY: Watson, Forbes. "A Note on Niles Spencer," *The Arts*, vol. 8, September 1925, pp. 166–169; "Painting and Sculpture by Living Americans," catalogue, Museum of Modern Art, 1930–1931; Cahill, Holger. "Niles Spencer," *Magazine of Art*, vol. 45, November 1952, pp. 313–315; "Niles Spencer," catalogue, University of Kentucky, 1965, essay by Richard B. Freeman.

168 *Buildings*. 1926. *
Oil on canvas, 24 × 30 in. (61 × 76.3 cm.).
Signed lower left "Niles Spencer."

EXHIBITIONS: Cincinnati Art Museum, 1935; Modern Art Society, Cincinnati, Ohio, "A New Realism," 12 March–7 April 1941, no. 32, p. 15; Carnegie Institute, 1952; Cincinnati Art Museum, Cincinnati, Ohio, 9 October–10 November 1953; Museum of Modern Art, New York, "Niles Spencer," circulating exhibition, 22 June–15 August 1954; University of Kentucky Art Gallery, Lexington, Kentucky, "The Works of Niles Spencer: Realism in American Painting," 10 October 1965–November 1966 and tour until June 1966 to Munson-Williams-Proctor Institute, Portland Museum, Maine, Whitney Museum, Allentown Art Museum, Pennsylvania, Currier Gallery of Art, New Hampshire, Museum of Art of Rhode Island School of Design, no. 42, illus. p. 65; University of New Mexico Art Museum, 1967, illus. p. 53.

169 *Corporation Shed*. 1928. *
Oil on canvas, 20 × 33 ¼ in. (50.8 × 84.5 cm.).
Signed lower left "Niles Spencer."

Spencer shared the Precisionists' preoccupation with translating native American scenes into an abstract, formalized vocabulary. In *Corporation Shed*, form and design are emphasized by utilizing geometric shapes and an arbitrary system of shading. The blank spaces, unconventional perspective and simple but monumental shapes evoke a sense of frozen movement and loneliness.

EXHIBITIONS: Philadelphia Museum of Art, Philadelphia, Pennsylvania, 1931; Modern Art Society, Cincinnati, Ohio, "A New Realism," 12 March–7 April 1941, no. 33, p. 15; Allen Memorial Art Museum, Oberlin College, Oberlin, Ohio, 20 November 1950–10 September 1951; Cincinnati Art Museum, Cincinnati, Ohio, 9 October–10 November 1953; The Contemporary Arts Center of Cincinnati Art Museum and Dayton Art Institute, Ohio, "An American Viewpoint: Realism in the 20th Century," 10 October 1967–15 January 1958, illus.; Denison University, Granville, Ohio, "Modern American Painting," 15 September–15 November 1962; Corcoran Gallery, Washington, D.C., "The New Tradition," 27 April–2 June 1963, no. 95, illus. p. 34; Smithsonian Institution, Washington, D.C. "Roots of Abstract Art in America 1910–1930," 1 December 1965–16 January 1966, no. 158, illus.; Flint Institute of Arts, Flint, Michigan, "Realism Revisited," 27 April–30 May 1966; University of Kentucky Art Gallery, Lexington, Kentucky, "The Works of Niles Spencer: Realism in American Painting," 10 October 1965–November 1965, no. 50, illus. p. 66; Museum of Fine Arts, St. Petersburg, 1968.

REPRODUCED: Kootz, Samuel. *Modern American Painters*. New York, 1930, pl. 51; *Creative Art*, vol. 7, no. 1, July 1930, p. 61; *Formes* (American edition), no. XXI, January 1932; Brown, Milton. *American Painting from the Armory Show to the Depression*. Princeton, 1955, p. 123.

Abraham Walkowitz (1878–1965)

Born in Siberia in 1878. Came to New York in 1889. Lived in Manhattan and Brooklyn for rest of life. Supported himself as commercial artist. Studied at National Academy of Design, New York, with Walter Shirilaw. Was instructor at Educational Alliance, New York, in 1900 where his works were first shown. Exhibited at University Settlement House in 1902 and at the National Academy of Design in 1904. Went to France in 1906 where he saw the memorial exhibition of Cézanne's work in 1907 and met Picasso and Henri Rousseau. Also visited Rodin's studio and first saw Isadora Duncan perform. She was a frequent subject in his subsequent works. Returned to New York in 1907. Works shown in "First Modern Exhibition" at Haas Gallery in 1908 and at Stieglitz' "291" gallery in 1912; associated with Stieglitz until 1917. Exhibited in Armory Show of 1913. Went to Europe again in 1914. Works appeared in "Forum Exhibition," Anderson Galleries, 1916. Was Director of Society of Independent Artists from 1918 to 1920. Travelled abroad in 1931. Was director of Société Anonyme in 1934. Had retrospective at Brooklyn Museum in 1939 and show of drawings and paintings at Jewish Museum, New York in 1949. Died in Brooklyn in 1965.

BIBLIOGRAPHY: Walkowitz, Abraham. *One Hundred Drawings and Paintings*. New York, 1925; "One Hundred Artists and Walkowitz," catalogue, Brooklyn Museum, February–March 1944; Walkowitz, Abraham. *Art from Life to Life*. Girard, Kansas 1951; Sawin, Martica. "Abraham Walkowitz, Artist," *Arts Magazine*, vol. 38, no. 6, March 1964, pp. 42–45.

170 *Bathers Resting*. n.d. *
Water color, 15⅜ × 29⅜ in. (39 × 74.7 cm.).
Signed lower left "A. Walkowitz."

Walkowitz, an immigrant artist who spent his student days in Paris, exhibited at the cosmopolitan "291" gallery in New York. He had great admiration for the gallery's director Stieglitz, but felt he "didn't know much about inner things." For Walkowitz, "inner things" were the crucial element in art. He valued children's drawings for their intuitive directness and fresh vision, untrammeled by knowledge of style. *Bathers Resting* evinces a childlike spirit in the large shapes, lack of detail and awkward, stiff figures that appear to float slightly above the ground. Walkowitz' water colors also show evidence of his six years in Europe. Matisse's influence is notably apparent in *Bathers Resting*. Like Matisse, Walkowitz utilizes large, flat areas of color and rhythmic, flowing line to produce a unified surface.

EXHIBITIONS: Albany Institute, 1958; American Federation of Arts, New York, "Adventures in Collecting," October 1958–October 1960; Allentown Art Museum, Allentown, Pennsylvania, 1–18 April 1961.

171 *Trees and Flowers*. 1917.
Water color, 15½ × 29⅝ in. (39.4 × 75.3 cm.).
Signed and dated lower left "A. Walkowitz, 1917."

172 *Bathers*. n.d.
Water color, 15⅜ × 29⅜ in. (39 × 74.7 cm.).
Signed lower left "A. Walkowitz."

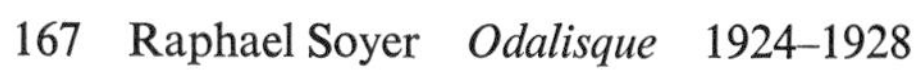

167 Raphael Soyer *Odalisque* 1924–1928

168 Niles Spencer *Buildings* 1926

169 Niles Spencer *Corporation Shed* 1928

170 Abraham Walkowitz *Bathers Resting* n.d.

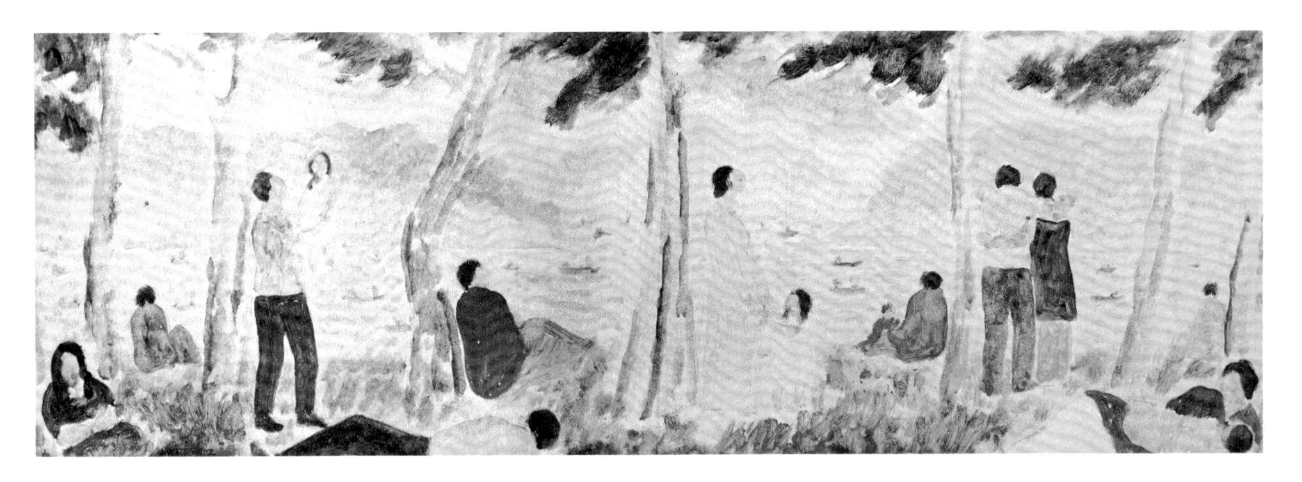

173 Abraham Walkowitz *Decoration, Figures in Landscape* n.d.

173 *Decoration, Figures in Landscape*. n.d. *
Water color and gouache, 12⅝ × 37 in. (32.1 × 93.9 cm.).
Signed lower left "A. Walkowitz."

EXHIBITIONS: Albany Institute, 1958.
REPRODUCED: *Arts*, vol. 8, August 1925, p. 94 (titled *Figures in Landscape*).

Max Weber (1881–1961)

Born in Russia in 1881. Came to U.S. in 1891. Graduated from Pratt Institute in 1900; previously had travelled to Paris with Arthur Wesley Dow, his teacher at Pratt. Returned to Paris in 1905 where he studied Persian miniatures, Coptic textiles and Greek and Oriental sculpture. Studied at Académie Julian, Académie Colarossi and La Grande Chaumière. Exhibited in Salon des Indépendents and Salon d'Automne. Helped organize small class to study with Matisse in 1907. Travelled in Spain in 1906 and Italy in 1907. Met Picasso and became a close friend of Henri Rousseau. Returned to New York in 1909 where he began an extended study of American Indian art. Had first one-man show at Haas Gallery and exhibited at "291" gallery that year. Arranged first American exhibition for Henri Rousseau at "291" gallery in 1910; had one-man show there in 1911 and at Murray Hill Galleries in 1912. Works shown at Alpine Club Gallery, London; his book, *Cubist Poems*, published in London in 1913. One-man show at Newark Museum in 1914 and at Montross Gallery, New York, in 1915. Taught at Art Students League in the 1920's. Exhibited at Société Anonyme after 1926. Second book of poetry, *Primitives*, published in 1926. Had retrospectives at several major museums in 1930's and 1940's including the Museum of Modern Art in 1930, Dayton Art Institute in 1938, and the Whitney Museum in 1949. Exhibited annually at Pennsylvania Academy of Fine Arts from 1946 until 1956. Worked as sculptor from 1958 to 1960. Died in 1961.

BIBLIOGRAPHY: Watson, Forbes. "The All-American Nineteen," *Arts*, vol. 16, January 1930, pp. 308–309; "Max Weber, Retrospective Exhibition," catalogue, Museum of Modern Art, March–April 1930, introduction by Alfred H. Barr, Jr.; Cahill, Holger. *Max Weber*. New York, 1930; Watson, Forbes. "Max Weber," *Magazine of Art*, vol. 34, February 1941, pp. 78–83; Weber, Max. *Max Weber*. American Artists Group, New York, 1945; "Max Weber Retrospective Exhibition," catalogue, Whitney Museum, February–March 1949, text by Lloyd Goodrich; "Max Weber," catalogue, Newark Museum, October–November 1959, introduction by William H. Gordts, Jr.; Werner, Alfred. "The Eternal Youth of Max Weber," *Painter & Sculptor*, vol. 3, no. 4, Winter 1960–1961, pp. 5–12; "Max Weber, Memorial Exhibition: 1881–1965," catalogue, Boston University, March 1962, introduction by Lillian Fortess; "Max Weber," catalogue, Art Galleries, University of California at Santa Barbara, February–March 1968.

174 *Still Life*. 1921. *
Oil on canvas, 15⅛ × 21⅛ in. (38.4 × 53.7 cm.).
Signed and dated lower right "Max Weber 1921."

Weber's early work, although eclectic, revealed his remarkable understanding of both modern and primitive art; he was able to assimilate the brilliance of the Fauves, the compositional complexity of the Cubists and the unusual coloring of Oriental and American Indian art. By 1917 however, he began to develop a more personal style that gave his later work an intensely expressive quality. In *Still Life*, his subjective, even poetic vision is manifest. Like Cézanne whom he greatly admired, Weber has reduced his forms to their basic structure, then distorted them in a manner that charges the picture with emotional energy.

EXHIBITIONS: Dayton Art Institute, 1941; Allen Memorial Art Museum, Oberlin College, Oberlin, Ohio, 20 November 1950–10 September 1951.

Stanton Macdonald Wright (1890–)

Born 1890, in Charlottesville, Virginia. Began painting when very young. Moved to Santa Monica, California, in 1900. Studied at Art Students League, Los Angeles, and privately with Joseph Greenbaum in 1904–1905. Went to Paris in 1907; studied at the Sorbonne and the Académie Colarossi, Académie Julian and the Ecole des Beaux Arts. Exhibited in Salon d'Automne, 1910, and the Salon des Independents, 1912. Met Morgan Russell in Paris in 1910 or 1911, and they pursued their interest in color theory together. Became interested in Oriental art in 1912. First Synchromist show held in 1913 at Neue Kunstsalon in Munich; subsequent shows in Paris, Milan, London and Warsaw. Returned to New York in 1913, where works appeared in the Armory Show that year. Synchromist canvases shown at Carroll Galleries, New York, in 1914. Went to Paris in 1914 with his brother, the critic Willard Huntington Wright, then to London, where they collaborated on several books later published in New York (see bibliography). Returned to New York in 1916 where works were shown at "291," Montross and Daniel galleries and in the Independent Artists Exhibition in 1917. Moved to Santa Monica in 1919 where he experimented with color film, producing the first full-length, stop-motion film in color. Directed Art Students League, Los Angeles, from 1922 to 1930. Studied Oriental art in the early 1920's, mastering Japanese and Chinese languages. Exhibited jointly with Morgan Russell in California and New York from 1927 to 1932. Spent 1931 in New York where he had a one-man show at Stieglitz' An American Place gallery. Returned to California in 1932. Was director of WPA art project in southern California from 1935 until 1937 when ill health caused him to spend a year convalescing in Japan; returned to WPA as technical advisor from 1938 to 1942; became interested in architectural decoration and mosaics during this period. Taught at UCLA and during the summer at the University of Southern California, Scripps College and the University of Hawaii. Went to Japan as Fulbright exchange professor in 1952 where he began collecting ancient Buddhist paintings. Returned to California the following year. Major retrospective held at Los Angeles City Museum in 1956; one-man shows in 1950's and 1960's at Rose Fried Gallery, New York, Esther Robles Gallery, Los Angeles, and others. Travelled to Europe and Japan in 1956 and 1958. Since 1958, often spends several months annually at a Zen monastery in Japan and, since the early 1960's, in Florence, Italy. Retrospective exhibition at the National Collection of Fine Arts, Washington, D.C. in 1967. Lives in California and Japan at present.

BIBLIOGRAPHY: Wright, Willard Huntington and Stanton Macdonald. *The Creative Will: Studies in the Philosophy and Syntax of Aesthetics*. New York, 1916; Wright, Willard Huntington and Stanton Macdonald. *The Future of Painting*. New York, 1923; Wright, Stanton Macdonald. *Approaches to Oriental and Occidental Art*. Honolulu, 1951; Agee, William. "Synchromism, The First American Movement," *Art News*, vol. 64, October 1965, p. 30; Wright, Stanton Macdonald. "The Artist Speaks: Stanton Macdonald Wright," with a note on synchromism by Barbara Rose, *Art in America*, vol. 55, no. 3, May–June 1967, pp. 70–73; "The Art of Stanton Macdonald-Wright," catalogue, National Collection of Fine Arts, Smithsonian Institution, May–June 1967, reprint of Wright's 1924 treatise on color.

175 *Still Life, No. 1*. n.d. *
Oil on pasteboard, 16 × 20 in. (40.6 × 50.8 cm.).
Signed upper right "Macdonald Wright."

EXHIBITIONS: Cincinnati Art Museum, 1935; National Collection of Fine Arts, Smithsonian Institution, Washington, D.C., "The Art of Stanton Macdonald-Wright," 4 May–18 June 1967.

176 *Still Life, No. 2*. 1917. *
Water color on pasteboard, 12½ × 15⅜ in.(31.8 × 39 cm.).
Signed and dated lower right "S Macdonald Wright, New York 1917."

Although similar in feeling to those of Demuth, Wright's still-life motifs were used as a point of departure for the expression of color relationships; he assigned each color a place in the total schema of the picture according to its "natural propensity." Wright studied the work of the 19th century color theorists Chevreul and Rood, as had the Post-Impressionists, but his adaptation of their principles to his own work was never dogmatic. In 1913, when the Synchromists exhibited in Paris for the first time, Wright and Morgan Russell wrote:

> We believe that the orientation towards color is the only direction that painters may, for the moment, be engaged in . . . It is the quality itself of form that we are trying to explain and reveal, and for the first time, here, color appears in this role.
>
> It is incumbent upon painters to deepen the rapport between color and form,—between colors and characteristics of form, its organic rhythm, its spatiality, luminosity, etc. Thus, having penetrated reality in a conscientious and lucid fashion, they will express the emotion of their discoveries by the language of color.

EXHIBITIONS: Los Angeles County Museum, Los Angeles, California, "A Retrospective Showing of the Work of Stanton Macdonald Wright," 19 January–19 February 1956, no. 6, p. 8; Albany Institute, 1958; American Federation of Arts, New York, "Adventures in Collecting," October 1958–October 1960; Allentown Art Museum, Allentown, Pennsylvania, 1–18 April 1961; Otterbein College, Westerville, Ohio, March 1965; National Collection of Fine Arts, Smithsonian Institution, Washington, D.C. "The Art of Stanton Macdonald-Wright," 4 May–18 June 1967, no. 11, illus. p. 31.

177 *California Landscape*. c. 1919. *
Oil on canvas, 29⅞ × 22⅛ in. (76 × 56.2 cm.).

Synchromism, a movement founded in Paris by Macdonald Wright and Morgan Russell in 1913, sought a positive orientation toward color, similar to the approach developed by the Orphists Delaunay and Kupka at about the same time.

Although Synchromism was fairly short-lived, it had a strong effect in America, inducing artists of such varied inclinations as Thomas Hart Benton, Arthur Davies and Patrick Henry Bruce to experiment more radically with the effects of color.

Macdonald Wright was convinced that color was essential in the expression of space and form, but he was not interested in total abstraction, as was Russell. He insisted that form must retain a close relationship with nature in order to remain expressive and diverse. Consequently, he used specific visual experiences, such as those gleaned from his visit to California in 1919, as a point of reference for theoretic investigations.

174 Max Weber *Still Life* 1921

175 Stanton Macdonald Wright
Still Life No. 1 n.d.

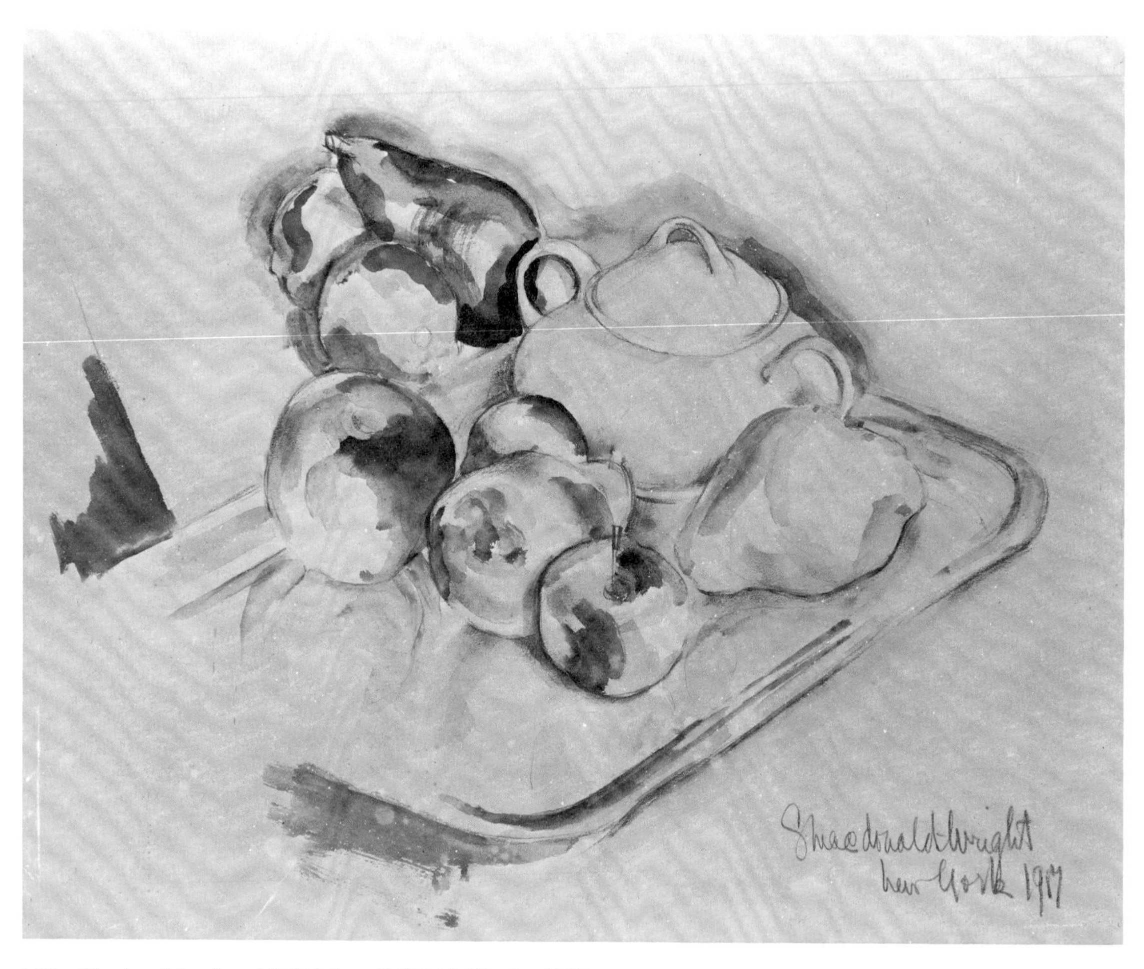

176 Stanton Macdonald Wright *Still Life No.* 2 1917

177 Stanton Macdonald Wright *California Landscape* c. 1919

178 William Zorach *The Fishermen* 1916

EXHIBITIONS: Carnegie Institute, 1952; University of Iowa, Iowa City, Iowa, "Summer Festival, Modern American Painting," 25 May–2 August 1962; Denison University, Granville, Ohio, "Modern American Painting," 15 September–15 November 1962; Corcoran Gallery, Washington, D.C. "The New Tradition," 27 April–2 June 1963, no. 68; Indiana University Museum of Art, Bloomington, Indiana, "American Painting 1910–1960," 19 April–10 May 1964, no. 44, illus.; Smithsonian Institution, Washington, D.C. "Roots of Abstract Art in America 1910–1930," 1 December 1965–16 January 1966, no. 102; National Collection of Fine Arts, Smithsonian Institution, Washington, D.C. "The Art of Stanton Macdonald-Wright," 4 May–18 June 1967, no. 9, illus. p. 28; Peale House of Pennsylvania Academy of the Fine Arts, Philadelphia, Pennsylvania, "Early Moderns Exhibition," 31 January–3 March 1968.

William Zorach (1887–1966)

Born in Lithuania 1887. Came to Ohio in 1891. Grew up in Cleveland where he worked as a lithographer's assistant from 1902 until 1906. Studied evenings at the Cleveland School of Art. Attended National Academy of Design, New York, for two winters around 1907–1909. Went to France in 1910; studied with Jacques Blanche in Paris and painted in southern France in the summer, 1911. Exhibited four works in Salon d'Automne in 1911. Returned to Ohio that year; supported himself as a lithographer. Had first one-man show at Taylor Galleries, Cleveland, in 1912, the year he moved to New York. Began spending summer months in Provincetown, Massachusetts, where he designed stage sets and helped produce O'Neill's first plays. Works exhibited in Armory Show, 1913. Began carving in 1917 while staying at a farmhouse in New Hampshire. Did sculpture exclusively after 1922, except for some water colors. Spent summers in Maine in 1920's, living in Brooklyn Heights, New York, in the winter. Taught sculpture at Art Students League from 1929 until his death. Lectured at Columbia University from 1932 until 1935. Retrospective exhibition at Whitney Museum, New York, in 1959. Died in 1966 in Maine.

BIBLIOGRAPHY: Wingert, Paul S. *The Sculpture of William Zorach*. New York, 1938; Zorach, William. *William Zorach*. American Artists Group, New York, 1945; Smith, Jacob Getler. "Another Side to William Zorach, His Water-colors," *American Artist*, vol. 22, no. 4, April 1958, pp. 20–27; Baur, John I. H. *William Zorach*. Whitney Museum, New York, 1959; Zorach, William. *Zorach Explains Sculpture*. New York, 1960; Zorach, William. *Art is My Life*. Cleveland, 1967.

178 *The Fishermen*. 1916. *
Water color, 11 × 8½ in. (28 × 21.6 cm.).
Signed and dated lower right "Wm. Zorach, 1916."

Zorach's water colors possess a vitality and charm lacking in the conservative, blocklike sculpture he executed after 1917.

His admiration for Cézanne is evident in *The Fishermen* where shapes are modelled to give equal emphasis to all areas of the picture plane. In this water color, a radical composition isolates and foreshortens the figures of the fishermen, whose translucent forms have bulk without weight.

EXHIBITIONS: Albany Institute, 1958; American Federation of Arts, New York, "Adventures in Collecting," October 1958–October 1960, no. 49; ACA American Heritage Gallery, New York, "50th Anniversary of the Forum Exhibition of Modern Painters March 1916," 14 March–9 April 1966, no. 41.

179 *Cart and Horse at Water's Edge*. 1916.
Water color, 11 × 8½ in. (28 × 21.6 cm.).
Signed and dated lower right "Wm. Zorach 1916–."

180 *Marine*. n.d.
Water color, 12¼ × 14½ in. (31 × 37 cm.).

General Bibliography *(listed chronologically)*

Books and Catalogues:

Rosenfeld, Paul. *Port of New York: Essays on Fourteen American Moderns.* New York, 1924.

Jewell, Edward A. *Americans.* New York, 1930.

Kootz, Samuel M. *Modern American Painters.* New York, 1930.

Barr, Alfred H., Jr. and Holger Cahill (eds.). *Art in America in Modern Times.* New York, 1934.

American Art Portfolios, Series One. New York, 1936.

Lane, James M. *Masters in Modern Art.* Boston, 1936.

"A New Realism: Crawford, Demuth, Sheeler, Spencer," catalogue, Cincinnati Art Museum, 1941.

Mellquist, Jerome. *The Emergence of an American Art.* New York, 1942.

Miller, Dorothy C. and Alfred H. Barr, Jr. (eds.). *American Realists and Magic Realists.* New York: Museum of Modern Art, 1943.

"The Eight," catalogue, Brooklyn Museum, 1944, foreword by John I. H. Baur and Everett Shinn.

Born, Wolfgang. *Still-Life Painting in America.* New York, 1947.

Soby, James T. *Contemporary Painters.* New York: Museum of Modern Art, 1948.

Larkin, Oliver W. *Art and Life in America.* New York, 1949.

Wight, Frederick S. *Milestones of American Painting in Our Century.* New York, 1949.

Baur, John I. H. *Revolution and Tradition in Modern American Art.* Cambridge: Harvard University Press, 1951.

Brown, Milton W. *American Painting from the Armory Show to the Depression.* Princeton: Princeton University Press, 1955.

Blesh, Rudi. *Modern Art U.S.A.: Men, Rebellion, Conquest, 1900–1956.* New York, 1956.

Richardson, Edgar P. *Painting In America.* New York, 1956.

Hunter, Sam. *Modern American Painting and Sculpture.* New York, 1959.

Friedman, Martin L. (text). "The Precisionist View in American Art," catalogue, Walker Art Center, Minneapolis, 1960.

Goodrich, Lloyd and John I. H. Baur. *American Art of Our Century.* New York, 1961.

Perlman, Bennard. *The Immortal Eight—American Painting from Eakins to the Armory Show.* New York, 1962.

Brown, Milton W. *The Story of the Armory Show.* New York: Joseph H. Hirshhorn Foundation, 1963.

Goodrich, Lloyd. *Pioneers of Modern Art in America: the Decade of the Armory Show, 1910–1920.* New York, 1963.

Geldzahler, Henry. *American Painting in the Twentieth Century.* New York, 1965.

Rose, Barbara. *American Art Since 1900, A Critical History.* New York, 1967.

Articles:

Rosenfeld, Paul. "American Painting," *The Dial*, vol. 71, December 1921, pp. 660–661, 649–670.

Formes (special American art number), no. 21, January 1932.

Benson, E. M. "The American Scene," *Magazine of Art*, vol. 27, no. 2, February 1934, pp. 53–66.

Cahill, Holger. "Forty Years After: An Anniversary for the A.F.A.," *Magazine of Art*, vol. 42, no. 5, May 1942, pp. 169–178, 189.

Brown, Milton. "Cubist-Realism: An American Style," *Marsyas*, New York University Institute of Fine Arts, vol. 3, 1943–45, pp. 139–159.

"Artists of the Philadelphia Press—William Glackens, George Luks, Everett Shinn, John Sloan," *Philadelphia Museum Bulletin*, vol. XLI, no. 207, October–November 1945, pp. 1–32.

McCausland, Elizabeth. "The Daniel Gallery and Modern American Art," *Magazine of Art*, vol. 44, no. 7, November 1951, pp. 280–285.

Brooks, V. "Eight's Battle for U.S. Art," *Art News*, vol. LIII, November 1954, pp. 41–43.

Hunter, Sam. "The Eight—Insurgent Realists," *Art in America*, vol. 44, no. 3, Fall 1956, pp. 20–22.

Art in America (issue on the Precisionists), vol. 48, no. 3, Fall 1960.

Smith, David L. "Romanticism and the American Tradition," *American Artist*, vol. XXVI, March 1962, pp. 32–33.

Weller, Allen S. "The Impressionists," *Art in America*, vol. 51, no. 3, 1963, pp. 86–92.

Art in America (issue on the Armory Show), vol. 51, no. 1, February 1963.

"Reaction and Revolution, 1900–1930," *Art in America*, vol. 53, no. 4, September 1965, pp. 68–87.

Index

Page numbers in parentheses refer to illustrations.

This book was composed and printed by
Clarke & Way, Inc., New York
Color separations by William Edmund Inc.
Moorestown, New Jersey
Format by the Bert Clarke Design Group